Answer Booklet with Solution CD Resource
Volume 2 (Chapters 21–33)
for
Tipler and Mosca's
Physics for Scientists and Engineers
Sixth Edition

David Mills
Professor Emeritus
College of the Redwoods

W. H. Freeman and Company
New York

© 2008 by W. H. Freeman and Company

ISBN-13: 978-1-4292-0457-6
ISBN-10: 1-4292-0457-5

Printed in the United States of America

First printing

W. H. Freeman and Company
41 Madison Avenue
New York, NY 10010
Houndmills, Basingstoke
RG21 6XS England
www.whfreeman.com

CONTENTS

Chapter 21
The Electric Field I: Discrete Charge Distributions

1   The net charge on large objects is always very close to zero. Hence the most obvious force is the gravitational force.

2   (c)

3   (a) Coulomb's law is only valid for point particles. The paper bits cannot be modeled as point particles because the paper bits become polarized.

   (b) No, the attraction does not depend on the sign of the charge on the comb. The induced charge on the paper that is closest to the comb is always opposite in sign to the charge on the comb, and thus the net force on the paper is always attractive.

4   (a) Connect the metal sphere to ground; bring the insulating rod near the metal sphere and disconnect the sphere from ground; then remove the insulating rod. The sphere will be negatively charged. (b) Bring the insulating rod in contact with the metal sphere; some of the positive charge on the rod will be transferred to the metal sphere.

5
   (a)

   (b)

6   Yes. Because a metal sphere is a conductor, the proximity of a positively charged ball (not necessarily a conductor) will induce a redistribution of charges on the metal sphere with the surface nearer the positively charged ball becoming negatively charged. Because the negative charges on the metal sphere are closer to the positively charged ball than are the positive charges on the metal sphere, the net force will be attractive.

7   Assume that the rod has a negative charge. When the charged rod is brought near the aluminum foil, it induces a redistribution of charges with the side nearer the rod becoming positively charged, and so the ball of foil swings toward the rod. When it touches the rod, some of the negative charge is transferred to the foil, which, as a result, acquires a net negative charge and is now repelled by the rod.

8   (*a*) A third positive charge can be placed midway between the fixed positive charges. This is the only location. (*b*) Yes. The position identified in (*a*) is one of stable equilibrium. It is stable in the *x* direction because, regardless of whether you displace the third positive charge to the right or to the left, the net force acting on it is back toward the midpoint between the two fixed charges. (*c*) If the third positive charge is displaced in the *y* direction, the net force acting on it will be away from its equilibrium position. Hence, the position midway between the fixed positive charges is one of unstable equilibrium in the *y* direction.

9   (*a*) On the sphere near the positively charged rod, the induced charge is negative and near the rod. On the other sphere, the net charge is positive and on the side far from the rod. This is shown in the diagram.

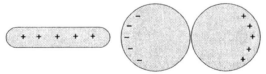

(*b*) When the spheres are separated and far apart and the rod has been removed, the induced charges are distributed uniformly over each sphere. The charge distributions are shown in the diagram.

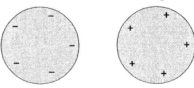

10   (*a*) to the right (*b*) zero

11   (*a*) False (*b*) True (*c*) False (*d*) Possibly (*e*) False (*f*) True

12   (*a*) False (*b*) True (*c*) False

13

(*a*)

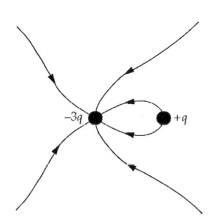

(*b*)

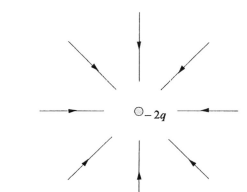

14 (*a*) $x_1 = \frac{\sqrt{3}}{6} a \; x_2 = \frac{\sqrt{3}}{2} a$ (*b*) $\vec{E}_P = kq \left[-\frac{1}{\left(\frac{\sqrt{3}}{2} a - x \right)^2} + \frac{2x}{\left(x^2 + \frac{1}{4} a^2 \right)^{3/2}} \right] \hat{i}$

(*c*) $\vec{E}_P(0) = -\frac{kq}{\left(\frac{\sqrt{3}}{2} a \right)^2} \hat{i}$, $\vec{E}_P\left(\frac{\sqrt{3}}{6} a \right) = 0$

15 The dipole moment rotates back and forth in oscillatory motion. The dipole moment gains angular speed as it rotates toward the direction of the electric field and loses angular speed as it rotates away from the direction of the electric field.

16 (*a*) False (*b*) False (*c*) False (*d*) True

17 Figure 21-23 shows the electric field due to a single dipole, where the dipole moment is directed toward the right. The electric field due to a pair of dipoles can be obtained by superposing the two electric fields.

3

	1	2	3
(a)	down	up	up
(b)	up	right	left
(c)	down	up	up
(d)	down	up	up

18 ≈ 0.2 kN

19 Because the can is grounded, the presence of the negatively charged plastic rod induces a positive charge on it. The positive charges induced on the can are attracted, via the Coulomb interaction, to the negative charges on the plastic rod. Unlike charges attract, so the can will roll toward the rod.

20 (a) 2.4×10^6 N/C (b) $E \propto T^{-1}$ (c) $E \propto P$

21 5.0×10^{12} electrons

22 9.63×10^4 C

23 4.82×10^7 C

24 (a) 1.99×10^{-15} % (b) 5.26×10^{-19} %

25 (a) 2.60 h (b) 2.1×10^{-13} W

26 (a) $\vec{F}_{1,2} = (24\,\text{mN})\hat{i}$ (b) $\vec{F}_{2,1} = (-24\,\text{mN})\hat{i}$ (c) $\vec{F}_{1,2} = (-24\,\text{mN})\hat{i}$, $\vec{F}_{2,1} = (24\,\text{mN})\hat{i}$

27 $\vec{F}_1 = (1.5 \times 10^{-2}\,\text{N})\hat{i}$

28 Between the point charges and a distance equal to $0.41L$ away from the $2.0\text{-}\mu\text{C}$ charge

29 A distance equal to $0.41L$ from the $-2.9\text{-}\mu\text{C}$ charge on the side away from the $4.0\text{-}\mu\text{C}$ charge

30 $\vec{F}_4 = (2.10 \times 10^{-5}\,\text{N})\hat{i} + (2.10 \times 10^{-5}\,\text{N})\hat{j}$

31 $\vec{F}_3 = -(8.65\,\text{N})\hat{j}$

32 -1.8 m, -0.91 m

33 $\vec{F}_1 = (0.90\,\text{N})\hat{i} + (1.8\,\text{N})\hat{j}$, $\vec{F}_2 = (-1.3\,\text{N})\hat{i} - (1.2\,\text{N})\hat{j}$,
$\vec{F}_3 = (0.4\,\text{N})\hat{i} - (0.64\,\text{N})\hat{j}$

34 $-3.00\,\mu\text{C}$

35 $\vec{F}_q = \dfrac{kqQ}{R^2}\left(1 + \sqrt{2}\right)\hat{i}$

36 $\vec{F}_2 = \vec{F}_3 = \vec{F}_1 = C\sqrt{6}\,\hat{k}$, $\vec{F}_4 = -3C\sqrt{6}\,\hat{k}$

37 (*a*) $(0.10\,\text{kN/C})\hat{i}$ (*b*) $(-0.36\,\text{kN/C})\hat{i}$

  (*c*)

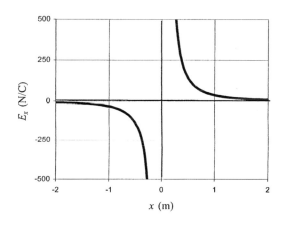

38 (*a*) $\vec{E}(-2.0\,\text{m}) = (-9.4\,\text{kN/C})\hat{i}$ (*b*) $\vec{E}(2.0\,\text{m}) = (8.0\,\text{kN/C})\hat{i}$
  (*c*) $\vec{E}(6.0\,\text{m}) = (-8.0\,\text{kN/C})\hat{i}$ (*d*) $\vec{E}(10\,\text{m}) = (9.4\,\text{kN/C})\hat{i}$ (*e*) $\vec{E}(4.0\,\text{m}) = 0$
  (*f*)

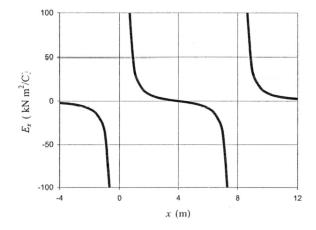

39   (a) $\vec{E}(0,0) = \left(4.0 \times 10^5 \text{ N/C}\right)\hat{j}$ (b) $\vec{F}(0,0) = \left(-1.6\,\text{mN}\right)\hat{j}$ (c) -40 nC

40   (a) $F_e = \left(2.69 \times 10^{12}\right)F_g$ (b) -0.196 mC

41   (a) 35 kN/C @ 0° (b) $\vec{F} = \left(69\,\mu\text{N}\right)\hat{i}$

42   2.4 cm

43   (a) 13 kN/C @ 230° (b) 2.1×10^{-15} N @ 51°

45   (a) 1.9 kN/C @ 230° (b) 3.0×10^{-16} N @ 230°

46   (b)

$2kq = 1$ and $a = 1$

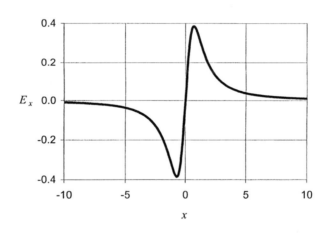

47   The charge must be placed a distance below the midpoint of the base of the triangle, where is the length of a side of the triangle.

48 $\frac{1}{4}q$

49   (a) For a positive test charge, the equilibrium at (0, 0) is unstable for small displacements in either direction along the axis, and stable for small displacements in either direction along the axis.

(b) For a negative test charge, the equilibrium is stable at (0,0) for displacements along the axis and unstable for displacements along the axis.

(c) $q_0 = -\frac{1}{4}q$

50 (b) $T = 2\pi\sqrt{\dfrac{ma^3}{2kq^2}}$

51 (a) 1.76×10^{11} C/kg (b) 1.76×10^{13} m/s^2 in the direction opposite the direction of the electric field (c) 0.2 μs (d) 3 mm

52 (a) 9.58×10^{11} C/kg, 1.76×10^{9} m/s^2 (b) 0.3 ms

53 (a) $\vec{a} = \left(-5.28 \times 10^{13}\ \text{m/s}^2\right)\hat{j}$ (b) 50.0 ns (c) 33.4° in the $-y$ direction

54 5.8 mm/s

55 800 μC

56 (a) 3.2 kN/C (b) 5.9 MN/C

57 The electron strikes the lower plate 4.1 cm to the right of its initial position.

58 (a) -6.40 mm (b) $-17.7°$ (c) -4.47 cm

59 (a) 8.0×10^{-18} C $\bullet$ m

(b)

60 (a) 0 (b) 3.2×10^{-24} N $\bullet$ m (c) 1.6×10^{-24} N $\bullet$ m (d) $U(0°) = -3.2 \times 10^{-24}$ J , $U(30°) = -2.8 \times 10^{-24}$ J

62 $\vec{E}_{P_1} = \left(1.14 \times 10^8\ \text{N/C}\right)\hat{i}$, $\vec{E}_{P_2} = \left(1.74 \times 10^6\ \text{N/C}\right)\hat{i}$, -6.95 cm, 0.417 cm

63 (a) 1.83×10^6 N/C (b) 1.80×10^6 N/C. The exact and estimated values of E_p agree to within 2%. This difference is this large because the separation of the two charges of the dipole is 20% of the distance from the center of the dipole to point P.

64 $T_1 = \dfrac{3kq^2}{d^2}$, $T_2 = \dfrac{9kq^2}{d^2}$

66 $2.99\,\mu C$

67 (a) 1.8×10^{-5} C and 1.8×10^{-4} C
(b) -1.4×10^{-5} C and 2.1×10^{-4} C

68 $m = \dfrac{qE}{g}$

69 (a) 0.225 N, downward (b) 0.112 N · m, counterclockwise (c) 45.8 g (d) 5.00×10^{-7} C

70 $-5.0\,\mu C$

71 (a) $28.0\,\mu C$ and $172\,\mu C$
(b) 250 N

72 (a) $-21.7\,\mu C$ and $222\,\mu C$
(b) 250 N

73 (a) $-97.2\,\mu C$ (b) $x = 0.0508$ m and $x = 0.169$ m

74 (b) $0.241\,\mu C$

75 (a) 10° (b) 9.9° for each

76 (a) $\vec{F}_1 = \dfrac{kq^2}{L^2}\left(1 - \dfrac{1}{2\sqrt{2}}\right)(\hat{i} + \hat{j})$

78 $55\,\mu C$

79 $v = \sqrt{\dfrac{ke^2}{2mL}}$

80 1.1×104 N/C, upward

82 $F = \dfrac{6kp^2}{d^4}$

83 (a) $E_y = \dfrac{2kQy}{\left[y^2 + \frac{1}{4}a^2\right]^{3/2}}$ (b) $\vec{F} = \dfrac{2kqQy}{\left[y^2 + \frac{1}{4}a^2\right]^{3/2}}\,\hat{j}$, where q is positive

(c) $v = \sqrt{8\left(1 - \sqrt{2/3}\right)}\sqrt{\dfrac{kqQ}{am}} = 1.21\sqrt{\dfrac{kqQ}{am}}$

84 1.48×10^7 m/s

85 4.6×10^{-14} m

86 (a) 4.8×10^{-19} C (b) 3 (c) 0.19 mm/s

87 (b) 52 μm/s

Chapter 22
The Electric Field II: Continuous Charge Distributions

1   The resultant field is directed along the dashed line, pointing away from the intersection of the two sides of the L-shaped object. This can be seen by dividing each leg of the object into 10 (or more) equal segments and then drawing the electric field on the dashed line due to the charges on each pair of segments that are equidistant from the intersection of the legs.

2   The electric fields along the lines defined by $y = x$ and $y = -x$ are the superposition of the electric fields due to the charge distributions along the axes. The direction of the electric field is the direction of the force acting on a test charge at the point(s) of interest. Typical points are shown at two points on each of the two lines.

3   (*a*) True (assuming there are no charges inside the shell) (*b*) True (*c*) False

4   No, this is not necessarily true. The only conclusion that we can draw is that there is equal positive and negative flux. For example, the net flux through a Gaussian surface completely enclosing a dipole is zero. If the electric flux is zero through the closed surface, we can conclude that the net charge inside the surface is zero.

5   (*a*) False (*b*) True

6   Because the net flux is proportional to the net charge enclosed, and this is the same for both surfaces, the electric flux through the surface of the cube is the same as the electric flux through the surface of the sphere.

7   (*a*) False (*b*) False (*c*) True (*d*) False (*e*) True

8   We can show that the charge inside a sphere of radius r is proportional to r^3 and that the area of a sphere is proportional to r^2. Using Gauss's law, it follows that the electric field must be proportional to $r^3/r^2 = r$.

9   (*a*) radially inward (*b*) radially outward (*c*) radially inward

10   (*b*)

11   (*a*) radially inward (*b*) radially inward (*c*) The field is zero.

12 (*a*) $\left|E_x\right|_{x=0.010\,cm} = 2.0\times10^5$ N/C, $\left|E_x\right|_{approx} = 2.0\times10^5$ N/C. The approximate value agrees to within 0.40% with the exact value and is larger than the exact value. (*b*) $\left|E_x\right|_{x=0.040\,cm} = 2.0\times10^5$ N/C. The approximate value agrees to within 1.2% with the exact value and is smaller than the exact value. (*c*) $\left|E_x\right|_{x=5.0\,m} = 2.5$ N/C, $\left|E_x(5.0\,m)\right|_{approx} = 2.5$ N/C. The approximate value agrees, to four significant figures, with the exact value.

13 (*a*) 18 nC (*b*) 26 N/C (*c*) 4.4 N/C (*d*) 2.6 mN/C (*e*) This result is about 0.01% less than the exact value obtained in (*d*).

14 (*a*) $\vec{E}_1 = -\left(3.4\times10^5 \text{ N/C}\right)\hat{i}$, $\vec{E}_2 = 0$, $\vec{E}_3 = \left(3.4\times10^5 \text{ N/C}\right)\hat{i}$ (*b*) $\vec{E}_1 = 0$, $\vec{E}_2 = \left(3.4\times10^5 \text{ N/C}\right)\hat{i}$, $\vec{E}_3 = 0$

(*c*)

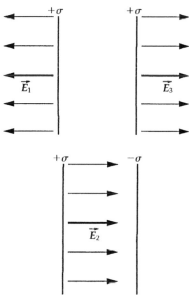

15 (*a*) 4.7×10^5 N/C (*b*) 1.1×10^6 N/C (*c*) 1.5×10^3 N/C (*d*) 1.5×10^3 N/C. This result agrees exactly, to two significant figures, with the result obtained in Part (*c*).

16 $x = R/\sqrt{3}$

17 (*a*) 0.189 kQ/a^2 (*b*) 0.358 kQ/a^2 (*c*) 0.385 kQ/a^2 (*d*) 0.354 kQ/a^2 (*e*) 0.179 kQ/a^2

(f)

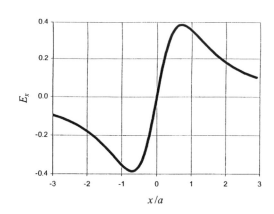

18 (a) $0.804\dfrac{\sigma}{2\,\epsilon_0}$ (b) $0.553\dfrac{\sigma}{2\,\epsilon_0}$ (c) $0.427\dfrac{\sigma}{2\,\epsilon_0}$ (d) $0.293\dfrac{\sigma}{2\,\epsilon_0}$

(e) $0.106\dfrac{\sigma}{2\,\epsilon_0}$

(f)

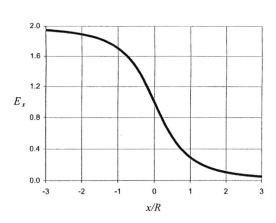

19

(a)

Cell	Content/Formula	Algebraic Form
B3	9.00E+09	k
B4	5.00E−10	σ
B5	0.3	r
A8	0	x_0
A9	0.01	$x_0 + 0.01$
B8	2*PI()*\$B\$3*\$B\$4*(1−A8/(A8^2+\$B\$5^2)^2)^0.5)	$2\pi k\sigma\left(1 - \dfrac{x}{\sqrt{x^2 + a^2}}\right)$
C8	2*PI()*\$B\$3*\$B\$4	$2\pi k\sigma$

	A	B	C
1			
2			
3	$k=$	9.00E+09	N·m^2/C^2
4	$\sigma=$	5.00E-10	C/m^2
5	$a=$	0.300	m
6			
7	x	$E(x)$	E_{sheet}
8	0.00	28.27	28.3
9	0.01	27.33	28.3
77	0.69	2.34	28.3
78	0.70	2.29	28.3

(*b*)

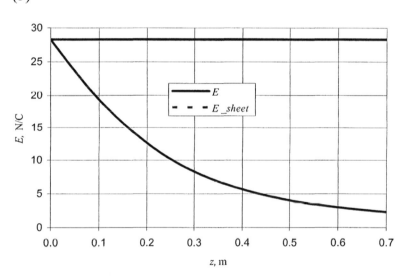

The magnitude of the electric fields differ by more than 10.0 percent for $x \geq 0.0300$ m.

20

(b)

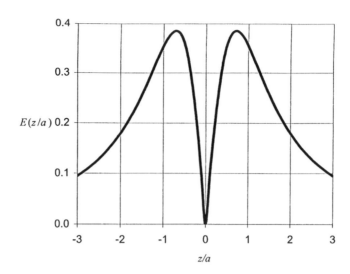

(c) $E_{x\max} = \dfrac{2\sqrt{3}}{9}\dfrac{kQ}{a^2}$

22 (a) $\vec{E} = -\dfrac{\pi k\lambda_0}{r}\,\hat{j}$ (b) The field at the origin is in the $-y$ direction and its magnitude is $\dfrac{\pi k\lambda_0}{r}$.

26 $E = \pi k\sigma$

27 (a) $20.0\ \text{N}\cdot\text{m}^2/\text{C}$ (b) $17\ \text{N}\cdot\text{m}^2/\text{C}$

28 (a)

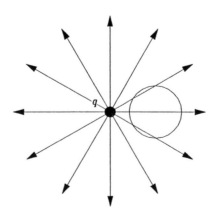

Given the number of field lines drawn from q, 3 lines enter the spherical surface. Had we chosen to draw 24 field lines, 6 would have entered the spherical surface.

(b) 3 (c) 0 (d) 0

29 (a) $1.5 \, \text{N} \cdot \text{m}^2/\text{C}$, $1.5 \, \text{N} \cdot \text{m}^2/\text{C}$ (b) 0 (c) $3.0 \, \text{N} \cdot \text{m}^2/\text{C}$ (d) $2.7 \times 10^{-11} \, \text{C}$

30 (a) $5.3 \times 10^{-8} \, \text{C}$ (b) You can only conclude that the net charge is zero. There may be an equal number of positive and negative charges present inside the box.

31 (a) $3.14 \, \text{m}^2$ (b) $7.19 \times 10^4 \, \text{N/C}$ (c) $2.26 \times 10^5 \, \text{N} \cdot \text{m}^2/\text{C}$ (d) No (e) 2.26×10^5 $\text{N} \cdot \text{m}^2/\text{C}$

32 $-5.65 \times 10^4 \, \text{N} \cdot \text{m}^2/\text{C}$

33 $-79.7 \, \text{nC}$

35 $\cos\theta$

36 $-1.2 \times 10^{-12} \, \text{C/m}^3$

37 (a) $\vec{E}_{r<R_1} = 0$, $\vec{E}_{R_1<r<R_1} = \dfrac{kq_1}{r^2}\hat{r}$, $\vec{E}_{r>R_2} = \dfrac{k(q_1+q_2)}{r^2}\hat{r}$ (b) -1

(c)

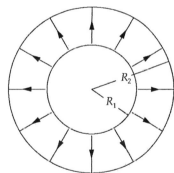

38 (a) $0.407 \, \text{nC}$ (b) 0 (c) 0 (d) $983 \, \text{N/C}$ (e) $366 \, \text{N/C}$

39 (a) $0.407 \, \text{nC}$ (b) $339 \, \text{N/C}$ (c) $1.00 \, \text{kN/C}$ (d) $983 \, \text{N/C}$ (e) $366 \, \text{N/C}$

40 (a) Because the outer sphere is conducting, the field in the thin shell must vanish. Therefore, $-2Q$, uniformly distributed, resides on the inner surface, and $-5Q$, uniformly distributed, resides on the outer surface.

(b) Now there is no charge on the inner surface and $-5Q$ on the outer surface of the spherical shell. The electric field just outside the surface of the inner sphere changes from a finite value to zero.

(*c*) In this case, the $-5Q$ is drained off, leaving no charge on the outer surface and $-2Q$ on the inner surface. The total charge on the outer sphere is then $-2Q$.

41 (*a*) $2.00 \ \mu C/m^3$ (*b*) 470 N/C

42 (*a*) $Q = \pi AR^4$ (*b*) $E_r(r > R) = \dfrac{AR^4}{4 \in_0 r^2}$, $E_r(r < R) = \dfrac{Ar^2}{4 \in_0}$

(*c*)

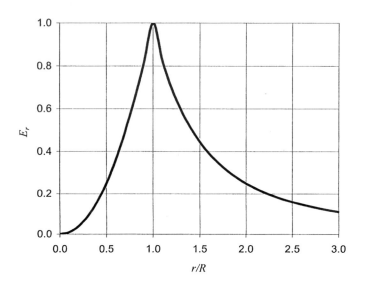

43 (*a*) $Q = 2\pi BR^2$ (*b*) $E_r = \dfrac{BR^2}{2 \in_0 r^2}$ $r > R$, $E_r = \dfrac{B}{2 \in_0}$ $r < R$

(*c*)

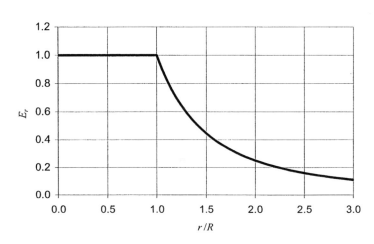

44 (a) $Q = 4\pi CR$ (b) $E_r = \dfrac{CR}{\epsilon_0\, r^2}\ r > R$, $E_r = \dfrac{C}{\epsilon_0\, r}\ r < R$

(c)

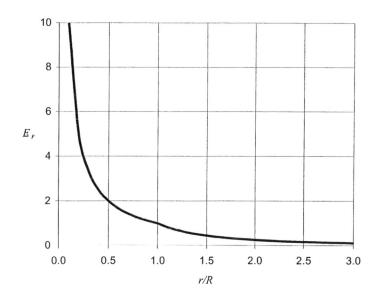

45 (a) $Q_{\text{inside}} = \dfrac{4\pi\rho}{3}\left(r^3 - R_1^3\right)$ (b) $E_r = 0\ r < R_1$,

$E_r = \dfrac{\rho}{3\,\epsilon_0\, r^2}\left(R_2^3 - R_1^3\right)\ \ R_1 < r < R_2$, $E_r = \dfrac{\rho}{3\,\epsilon_0\, r^2}\left(R_2^3 - R_1^3\right)\ \ r > R_2$

46 76.5 nC/m

47 (a) 4.1×10^7 m/s (b) Because of its much larger mass, the impact speed of the ion will be much less than the impact speed of the electron. (The ion will impact the tube instead of the wire.)

49 (a) 679 nC (b) 0 (c) 0 (d) 1.00 kN/C (e) 610 N/C

51 (a) 679 nC (b) 339 N/C (c) 1.00 kN/C (d) 1.00 kN/C (e) 610 N/C

52 (a) $E_R = 0\ r < R_1$, $E_R = \dfrac{\sigma_1 R_1}{\epsilon_0\, r}\ R_1 < r < R_2$, $E_R = \dfrac{\sigma_1 R_1 + \sigma_2 R_2}{\epsilon_0\, r}\ r > R_2$

(b) $\dfrac{\sigma_1}{\sigma_2} = -\dfrac{R_2}{R_1}$ (c) $E_R = \dfrac{\sigma_1 R_1}{\epsilon_0\, r}\ R_1 < r < R_2$

(*d*)

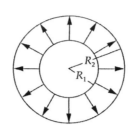

53 (*a*) $E_R = 0 \quad r < 1.50\,\text{cm}, E_R = \dfrac{(108\,\text{N}\cdot\text{m/C})}{r} \quad 1.50\,\text{cm} < r < 4.50\,\text{cm}$,

$E_R = 0 \quad 4.50\,\text{cm} < r < 6.50\,\text{cm}, \quad E_R = \dfrac{156\,\text{N}\cdot\text{m/C}}{r} \quad r > 6.50\,\text{cm}$

(*b*) $\sigma_{\text{inside}} = -21.2\,\text{nC/m}^2$ and $\sigma_{\text{outside}} = 14.7\,\text{nC/m}^2$

54 (*b*) $E_R = \dfrac{a}{3\,\epsilon_0} r^2 \quad r < R, \; E_R = \dfrac{aR^3}{3r\,\epsilon_0} \quad r > R$

55 (*b*) $E_R = \dfrac{b}{4\,\epsilon_0} r^3 \quad r < a, \; E_R = \dfrac{bR^4}{4r\,\epsilon_0} \quad r > a$

56 $E_R = 0 \; r < R_1, E_R = \dfrac{\rho\left(r^2 - R_1^2\right)}{2\,\epsilon_0\, r} \quad R_1 < r < R_2, E_R = \dfrac{\rho\left(R_2^2 - R_1^2\right)}{2\,\epsilon_0\, r} \quad r > b$

57 (*a*) 18.8 nC/m (*b*) $E_R = 22.6\,\text{kN/C} \; R < 1.50\,\text{cm}$,

$E_R = \dfrac{339\,\text{N}\cdot\text{m/C}}{R} \quad 1.50\,\text{cm} < R < 4.50\,\text{cm}, \; E_R = 0 \quad 4.50\,\text{cm} < R < 6.50\,\text{cm}$,

$E_R = \dfrac{339\,\text{N}\cdot\text{m/C}}{R} \quad R > 6.50\,\text{cm}$

58 (*a*) 14.2 nC/m^2 (*b*) 4.45 pC

59 9.4 kN/C

60 (*a*) −150 nC/m^2 (*b*) 8.47 kN/C. The direction of the field on the side of the sheet that is charged is the direction of the electric force acting on a test charge. Because the surface is negatively charged, this force and, hence, the electric field, is directed toward the surface. Because the sheet is constructed from non-conducting material, no charge is induced on the second surface of the sheet and there is, therefore, no electric field just outside the sheet surface on this side.

61   (a) $E_r = \dfrac{kq}{r^2}$ $r < R_1$, $E_r = 0$ $R_1 < r < R_2$, $E_r = \dfrac{kq}{r^2}$ $r > R_2$

(b)

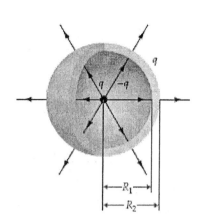

(c) $\sigma_{inner} = -\dfrac{q}{4\pi R_1^2}$, $\sigma_{outer} = \dfrac{q}{4\pi R_2^2}$

62   (a) negative (b) 677 kC

63   (a) $\sigma_{inner} = -0.55\,\mu\text{C/m}^2$, $\sigma_{outer} = 0.25\,\mu\text{C/m}^2$

(b) $E_r = \left(2.3 \times 10^4\ \text{N}\cdot\text{m}^2/\text{C}\right)\dfrac{1}{r^2}$ $r < 0.60$ m, $E_r = 0$ $0.60\,\text{m} < r < 0.90\,\text{m}$,

$E_r = \left(2.3 \times 10^4\ \text{N}\cdot\text{m}^2/\text{C}\right)\dfrac{1}{r^2}$ $r > 0.90$ m

(c) $\sigma_{inner} = -0.55\,\mu\text{C/m}^2$, $\sigma_{outer} = 0.59\,\mu\text{C/m}^2$,

$E_r = \left(2.3 \times 10^4\ \text{N}\cdot\text{m}^2/\text{C}\right)\dfrac{1}{r^2}$ $r < 0.60$ m, $E_r = 0$ $0.60\,\text{m} < r < 0.90\,\text{m}$,

$E_r = \left(5.4 \times 10^4\ \text{N}\cdot\text{m}^2/\text{C}\right)\dfrac{1}{r^2}$ $r > 0.90$ m

64   23 cm

65   (a) $Q_{\text{left}} = 15\,\mu\text{C}$, $Q_{\text{right}} = 65\,\mu\text{C}$ (b) $\vec{E}_{\text{left}\,x} = -68\,\text{kN/C}$ and

$\vec{E}_{\text{right}\,x} = 294\,\text{kN/C}$, $\sigma_{\text{left}} = 0.60\,\mu\text{C/m}^2$ and $\sigma_{\text{right}} = 2.60\,\mu\text{C/m}^2$

66   (a) Toward the center. (b) $+Q_0$ (c) $-Q_0$ (d) $+Q_0$ (e) 0

(f)

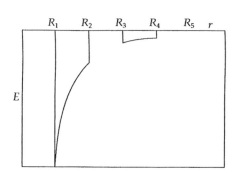

67   -115 kN/C

68   $\vec{E}(2.00\,\text{m}, 1.50\,\text{m}) = (1.62\,\text{kN/C})\,\hat{i} - (4.18\,\text{kN/C})\,\hat{j}$

69   (a) $E = \dfrac{Q}{8\pi\,\epsilon_0\,r^2}$ radially outward (b) $F = \dfrac{Q^2 a^2}{32\pi\,\epsilon_0\,r^4}$ radially outward

(c) $P = \dfrac{Q^2}{32\pi^2\,\epsilon_0\,r^4}$

70   (a) $\vec{E}(6.0\,\text{m}, 2.0\,\text{m}) = (1.3\,\text{kN/C})\,\hat{i} + (1.5\,\text{kN/C})\,\hat{j}$
     (b) $\vec{E}(6.0\,\text{m}, 5.0\,\text{m}) = (-1.3\,\text{kN/C})\,\hat{i} + (5.9\,\text{kN/C})\,\hat{j}$

71   (a) 339 kN/C toward the right (b) 339 kN/C toward the right (c) zero (d) zero

72   (a) 339 kN/C @ 0° (b) 1.34 MN/C @ 348° (c) 203 kN/C @ 0°

73   (a) $\rho_0 = \dfrac{-e}{\pi a^3}$ (b) $E_r(r) = \dfrac{ke}{r^2}\left(1 - \dfrac{1}{4}\left[\left(1 - e^{-2r/a}\right) - 2e^{-2r/a}\left(\dfrac{r}{a} + \dfrac{r^2}{a^2}\right)\right]\right)$

74   (a) $\dfrac{q}{m} = \dfrac{\sqrt{27}\,ga^2}{2kQ}$ (b) $z = -0.205a$ and $z = -1.90a$

75   (a) radially outward toward the gap (b) $E_{\text{center}} = \dfrac{kQ\ell}{2\pi R^3}$

76   (a) 94 kN/C @ 0° (b) 33.6 kN/C @ 90° (c) 15.6 kN/C @ 304°

77   (a) $\vec{E} = 204\,\text{kN/C}$ at 56.3° (b) $\vec{E} = 263\,\text{kN/C}$ at 153°

78 $E = 241 \, \text{kN/C} \, @ \, 220°$

79   (a) $v = \sqrt{\dfrac{2kq\lambda}{m}}$ (b) $T = \pi R \sqrt{\dfrac{2m}{kq\lambda}}$

80   (b) $F_x = \dfrac{kqQ}{a^3} x$ (d) $f = \dfrac{1}{2\pi} \sqrt{\dfrac{kqQ}{ma^3}}$

81   (a) 0.997 kg (b) 1.18 Hz

82   Yes. The frequency changes by a factor of 0.5.

83   (b) $\vec{E}_1 = \vec{E}_2 = \dfrac{\rho b}{3 \epsilon_0} \hat{i}$

85 $\vec{E}_1 = \left(\dfrac{\rho b}{3 \epsilon_0} + \dfrac{Q}{4\pi \epsilon_0 b^2} \right) \hat{i}$, $\vec{E}_2 = \left(\dfrac{\rho b}{3 \epsilon_0} - \dfrac{Q}{4\pi \epsilon_0 b^2} \right) \hat{i}$

87   ½ R

88 $F = - \dfrac{2k\lambda p}{r^2}$

Chapter 23
Electric Potential

1 The proton is moving to a region of higher potential. The proton's electrostatic potential energy is increasing.

2 The electron is moving to a region of higher electric potential. The electron's electrostatic potential energy is decreasing.

3 The electric field is zero throughout the region.

4 No. $\vec{E}$ can be determined without knowing V at a continuum of points.

5

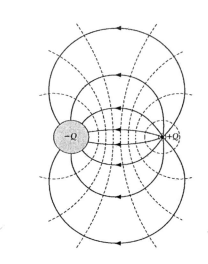

6

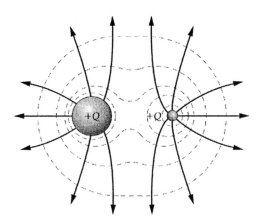

7

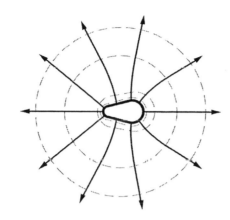

8

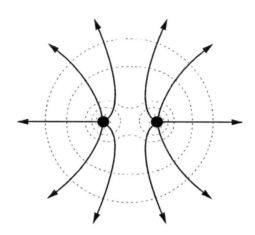

9   (*a*) 2 (*b*) 3

10

(*a*)

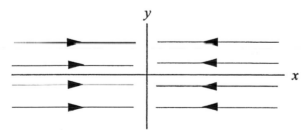

(*b*) 1. Field lines end on negative charges.

11   No. The local surface charge density is proportional to the normal component of the electric field, not the potential on the surface.

12 4

13 3.0×10^9 V

14 2.0 kV

15 0.72 MeV

16 6.0 kV

17 27 μC/m^2

18 (*a*) 2.66 nC/m^2 (*b*) 1.35 MC (*c*) 1.91 GV (*d*) about 2.2 h

19 (*a*) 4.49 kV (*b*) 13.5 mJ

20 (*a*) The positive plate is at the higher potential. (*b*) 5.00 kV/m
(*c*) 8.01×10^{-17} J, 500 eV (*d*) − 500 eV (*e*) 500 eV

21 (*a*) −8.00 kV (*b*) − 24.0 mJ (*c*) 24.0 mJ (*d*) $V(x) = -(2.00\,\text{kV/m})x$

22 (*a*) 5.14 eV (*b*) 5.14 eV

23 (*a*) 3.09×10^7 m/s (*b*) 2.50 MV/m

24 (*a*) Because positively charged objects are accelerated from higher-potential
to lower-potential regions, the screen must be at the higher electric potential
to accelerate electrons toward it. (*b*) 3.00×10^4 eV, 4.81×10^{-15} J

25 (*a*) $r = kzZe^2/K_i$ (*b*) 46 fm, 25 fm (*c*) No. The distance of closest approach
for a 5-MeV alpha particle found above (46 fm) is much larger than the 7 fm
radius of a gold nucleus. Hence, the scattering was solely the result of the
inverse-square Coulomb force.

26 (*a*) 25.4 kV (*b*) 12.7 kV (*c*) 0

27 (*a*) 12.9 kV (*b*) 7.55 kV (*c*) 4.43 kV

28 (*a*) 12.0 kV (*b*) 59.9 mJ (*c*) 59.9 mJ

29 (*a*) 135 kV (*b*) 95.3 kV (*c*) Because the two field points are equidistant
from all points on the circle, the answers for parts (*a*) and (*b*) would not
change.

30   (a) 2 (b) 2 (c) $-\frac{1}{2}$

31   (a) $V = kq\left(\dfrac{1}{|x-a|} + \dfrac{1}{|x+a|}\right)$

(b)

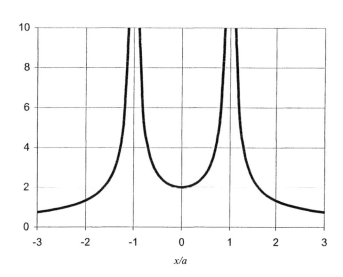

32

(a)

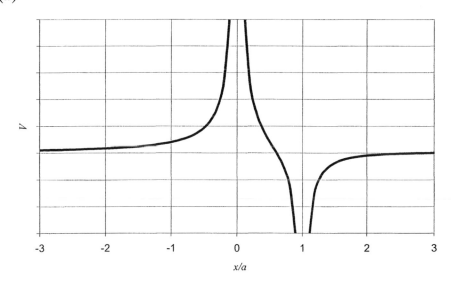

(b) $\pm\infty$, $3a$, $0.6a$ (c) $5.4a$, $0.55a$ (d) $W = \dfrac{2ke^2}{a}$

33   (b) at points on the z axis

35 (*a*) positive (*b*) 25.0 kV/m

36 −7.50 kV. The point at $x = 2.00$ m is at the higher potential.

37 (*a*) +668 nC (*b*) 3.00 kV. The point at $x = 2.00$ m is at the higher potential.

38 4.5 m. At this location, the potential is not zero. The electric field is zero when the slope of the potential function is zero.

39 (*a*) $V(x) = kq\left(\dfrac{2}{\sqrt{x^2 + a^2}} + \dfrac{1}{|x - a|} \right) \qquad x \neq a$

    (*b*) $E_x(x) = \dfrac{2kqx}{\left(x^2 + a^2\right)^{3/2}} + \dfrac{kq}{\left(x - a\right)^2} \qquad x > a,$

    $E_x(x) = \dfrac{2kqx}{\left(x^2 + a^2\right)^{3/2}} - \dfrac{kq}{\left(a - x\right)^2} \qquad x < a$

40 (*a*) $\vec{E}(r < 12.0\,\text{cm}) = 0$, $E(r > 12.0\,\text{cm}) = 6.24\,\text{MV/m}$ (*b*)
    $V(r \leq R) = 749\,\text{kV}$, $V(r \geq R) = 749\,\text{kV}$ (*c*) $V(r \leq R) = 749\,\text{kV}$ (*d*) 0

41 (*a*) 6.02 kV (*b*) −12.7 kV (*c*) −42.3 kV

42 (*a*) about 9 μC (*b*) $\pm 5 \times 10^5$ V

43 $\sim 3 \times 10^{-5}$ C/m^2

44 (*a*) 0 (*b*) $V_a = kQ\left(\dfrac{1}{a} - \dfrac{1}{b} \right)$

45 $V_a - V_b = \dfrac{2kq}{L} \ln\left(\dfrac{b}{a} \right)$

46 $\sigma_{12\text{cm}} = 1.77\,\mu\text{C/m}^2$, $\sigma_{5\text{cm}} = 4.25\,\mu\text{C/m}^2$

47 $V_a - V_b = kq\left(\dfrac{1}{a} - \dfrac{1}{b} \right)$

48 10.0 cm, 5.01 nC

49

Region	$x \leq 0$	$0 \leq x \leq a$	$x \geq a$
Part (a)	$\dfrac{\sigma}{\epsilon_0} x$	0	$-\dfrac{\sigma}{\epsilon_0}(x-a)$
Part (b)	0	$-\dfrac{\sigma}{\epsilon_0} x$	0

51   (a) $V(x,0) = \dfrac{kQ}{L} \ln\left(\dfrac{\sqrt{x^2 + \frac{1}{4}L^2} + \frac{1}{2}L}{\sqrt{x^2 + \frac{1}{4}L^2} - \frac{1}{4}L^2} \right)$

52   (a) $V(x,0) = \dfrac{kQ}{L}\left[\ln\left(\dfrac{L + \sqrt{x^2 + L^2}}{x} \right) \right]$

53   (a) $Q = \frac{1}{2}\pi\sigma_0 R^2$ (b) $V = \dfrac{2\pi k\sigma_0}{R^2}\left(\dfrac{R^2 - 2x^2}{3}\sqrt{x^2 + R^2} + \dfrac{2x^3}{3} \right)$

54   (a) $Q = 2\pi\sigma_0 R^2$ (b) $V = 2\pi k\sigma_0 R \ln\left(\dfrac{R + \sqrt{x^2 + R^2}}{x} \right)$

55   (a) $V(x) = \dfrac{kQ}{L} \ln\left(\dfrac{x + \frac{1}{2}L}{x - \frac{1}{2}L} \right)$

56   (a) $V = 2\pi k\sigma\left(\sqrt{x^2 + b^2} - \sqrt{x^2 + a^2} \right)$

57   (a) $dQ = \dfrac{3Q}{R^3} r'^2 dr'$ (b) $dV = \dfrac{3kQ}{R^3} r' dr'$ (c) $V = \dfrac{3kQ}{2R^3}\left(R^2 - r^2 \right)$

      (d) $dV = \left(\dfrac{3kQ}{R^3 r} \right) r'^2\, dr'$ (e) $V = \dfrac{kQ}{R^3} r^2$ (f) $V = \dfrac{kQ}{2R}\left(3 - \dfrac{r^2}{R^2} \right)$

58    $V = \dfrac{kQ}{R}$

60   0.506 mm

61   (a) The equipotential surfaces are planes parallel to the charged planes.

      (b) The regions to either side of the two charged planes are equipotential regions, so any surface in either of these regions is an equipotential surface.

62   (a) The electric field is directed radially away from the central wire.

(b) The central wire is at the higher electric potential.

(c) The equipotential surfaces are cylinders concentric with the central wire.

(d) No. Because the magnitude of the electric field, which is the rate of change with distance (also known as the gradient) of the potential decreases with distance from the wire, the spacing between adjacent equipotential surfaces having the same potential difference between them decreases as you get farther from the central wire.

63 (a) 0.224 cm, closer to the wire (b) 0.864 mm (c) The distance between the 700 V and the 725 V equipotentials is 0.0966 mm. This closer spacing of these two equipotential surfaces was to be expected. Close to the central wire, two equipotential surfaces with the same difference in potential should be closer together to reflect the fact that the electric field strength is greater closer to the wire.

64 (a) The equipotential surfaces are spheres centered on the charge.
(b)

V (V)	20.0	40.0	60.0	80.0	100.0
r (m)	4.99	2.49	1.66	1.25	1.00

(c) No. The equipotential surfaces are closest together where the electric field strength is greatest.

(d) $E_{est} = 29$ V/m, $E_{exact} = 23$ V/m. The estimated value for E differs by about 21% from the exact value.

65 (a) 30.0 mJ (b) −5.99 mJ (c) −18.0 mJ

66 (a) 190 mJ (b) −63.4 mJ (c) −63.4 mJ

67 (a) 22.3 nC (b) 22.3 μJ

68 (a) 48.7 mJ (b) 0 (c) −12.7 mJ (d) −23.2 mJ

69 $v = q\sqrt{\dfrac{6\sqrt{2}k}{ma}} = 2.91q\sqrt{\dfrac{k}{ma}}$

70 (a) 960 keV (b) 240 keV (c) 9.59×10^6 m/s

71   (a) 9.61×10^{-20} J (b) 4.59×10^{5} m/s (c) Because $2K_{i\,min} > K_{i\,escape}$, the electron escapes from the proton with residual kinetic energy.

72   0

73   (a) $V(x) = \dfrac{2kq}{\sqrt{x^2 + a^2}}$ (b) $\vec{E}(x) = \dfrac{2kqx}{\left(x^2 + a^2\right)^{3/2}} \hat{i}$

74   about 3 mm

75   (a) $V(x, y) = \dfrac{\lambda}{2\pi \epsilon_0} \ln\left(\dfrac{\sqrt{(x-a)^2 + y^2}}{\sqrt{(x+a)^2 + y^2}} \right)$, $V(0, y) = 0$

(b) $y = \pm\sqrt{21.25x - x^2 - 25}$

(c)

Cell	Content/Formula	Algebraic Form
A2	1.25	$\frac{1}{4}a$
A3	A2 + 0.05	$x + \Delta x$
B2	SQRT(21.25*A2 − A2^2 − 25)	$y = \sqrt{21.25x - x^2 - 25}$
B4	− B2	$y = -\sqrt{21.25x - x^2 - 25}$

	A	B	C
	x	y_{pos}	y_{neg}
2	1.25	0.00	0.00
3	1.30	0.97	−0.97
4	1.35	1.37	−1.37
5	1.40	1.67	−1.67
6	1.45	1.93	−1.93
7	1.50	2.15	−2.15
370	19.65	2.54	−2.54
371	19.70	2.35	−2.35
372	19.75	2.15	−2.15
373	19.80	1.93	−1.93
374	19.85	1.67	−1.67
375	19.90	1.37	−1.37
376	19.95	0.97	−0.97

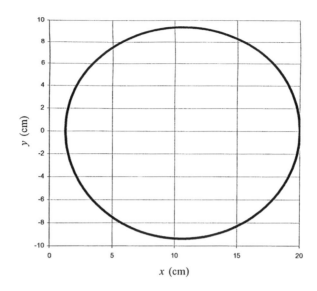

76 (b) The three-dimensional surfaces are cylinders whose axes are parallel to the wires and are in the $y = 0$ plane.

77 (a) 3.56×10^8 C/m^3 (b) $V(r) = \pi k a^3 \rho_0 \left(\dfrac{1}{a} + \dfrac{1}{r} \right) e^{-2r/a} = ke \left(\dfrac{1}{a} + \dfrac{1}{r} \right) e^{-2r/a}$

78 250 W

79 (a) $W_{+Q \to +a} = \dfrac{kQ^2}{2a}$ (b) $W_{-Q \to 0} = \dfrac{-2kQ^2}{a}$ (c) $W_{-Q \to 2a} = \dfrac{2kQ^2}{3a}$

80 1.4×10^{-7} J , 9.0×10^{11} eV

81 (a) 100 eV (b) 1.38×10^5 m/s

82

(a)

Cell	Content/Formula	Algebraic Form
A4	A3 + 0.1	$z + \Delta z$
B3	1/(1+A3^2)^(1/2)	$\dfrac{kQ}{\sqrt{a^2 + z^2}}$

	A	B
1		
2	z/a	$V(z/a)$
3	−5.0	0.196
4	−4.8	0.204
52	4.8	0.204
53	5.0	0.196

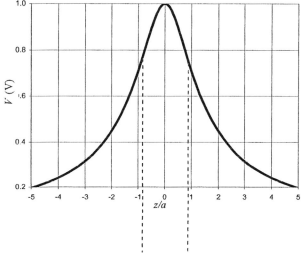

(b) Examining the graph we see that the magnitude of the slope is maximum at $z/a = 0.7$ and at $z/a = -0.7$.

83 $R_2 = \dfrac{2}{3} R_1$

84 (a) 60.0 cm (b) The charge on the sphere is positive.

85 7.1 nC

86 44.6 fm

87 (b) $\sigma = \dfrac{qd}{4\pi \left(d^2 + r^2\right)^{3/2}}$

88 (a) $V(x) = \dfrac{kQ}{\sqrt{(x+L)^2 + L^2}} + \dfrac{kQ}{\sqrt{(x-L)^2 + L^2}}$ (d) $\omega - \dfrac{1}{2}\sqrt{\dfrac{\sqrt{2}kqQ}{mL^3}}$

89 (a) $V(c) = 0$, $V(b) = kQ\left(\dfrac{1}{b} - \dfrac{1}{c}\right)$, $V(a) = V(b) = kQ\left(\dfrac{1}{b} - \dfrac{1}{c}\right)$

(b) $Q_b = Q$, $V(a) = V(c) = 0$, $Q_a = -Q\dfrac{a(c-b)}{b(c-a)}$, $Q_c = -Q\dfrac{c(b-a)}{b(c-a)}$,

$V(b) = kQ\dfrac{(c-b)(b-a)}{b^2(c-a)}$

90 $q = -\dfrac{a}{b}Q$

92 (a) 1.69 fm. This model does not explain how the electron holds together against its own mutual repulsion. (b) 9.21×10^{-19} m. This result is way too small to agree with the experimental value of 1.2×10^{-15} m.

93 (a) $R' = 0.794R$ (b) $\Delta E = -0.370E$

94 428 MeV

Chapter 24
Capacitance

1   (*c*)

2   (*c*)

3   False. The electrostatic energy density is not uniformly distributed because the magnitude of the electric field strength is not uniformly distributed.

4   2

5   1/3

6   3

7   (*a*) True (*b*) True

8   (*a*) False. Capacitors connected in series carry the same charge Q. (*b*) False. The voltage V across a capacitor whose is Q/C. (*c*) False. The energy stored in a capacitor is given by $\frac{1}{2}QV$. (*d*) False. This would be the equivalent capacitance if they were connected in parallel. (*e*) True. Taking the reciprocal of the sum of the reciprocals of C_0 and $2C_0$ yields $C_{eq} = 2C_0/3$.

9   (*a*) True (*b*) False. Because $Q = CV$ and C increases, Q must increase. (*c*) True. $E = V/d$ where d is the plate separation. (*d*) False. $U = \frac{1}{2}QV$.

10   $C_A > C_B$

11   (*a*) $U_{parallel} = 2U_{1\,capacitor}$ (*b*) $U_{series} = \frac{1}{2}U_{1\,capacitor}$

12   (*d*)

13   $0.1\,\text{nF/m} \le C/L \le 0.2\,\text{nF/m}$

14   22 μF

15   2.3 nF

16   (*a*) 22.3 nC (*b*) 11.1 pF (*c*) It doesn't.

17   75.0 nF

18 $C = 2\pi \epsilon_0 R$

19   (a) 15.0 mJ (b) 45.0 mJ

20   (a) 0.80 μJ (b) 0.20 μJ

21   (a) 0.625 J (b) 1.88 J

22   40 J/m^3

23   (a) 100 kV/m (b) 44.3 mJ/m^3 (c) 88.5 μJ (d) 17.7 nF (e) 88.5 μJ

24   (a) 0.6 μJ (b) 0.2 nF (c) 0.05 μJ, a result that agrees to within 5% with the exact result obtain in (a).

25   (a) 11 nC (b) Because work has to be done to pull the plates farther apart, you would expect the energy stored in the capacitor to increase. (c) 0.55 μJ

26   (a) 100

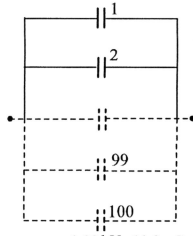

(b) 10.0 V (c) $V_{\text{series combination}} = 1.00 \, \text{kV}$, 10.0 μC

27   10.00 μF

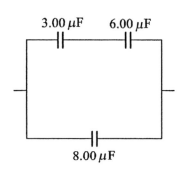

28 $C_{eq} = C_2 + \dfrac{C_1 C_3}{C_1 + C_3}$

29 (a) 30.0 μF (b) 6.00 V (c) $Q_{10} = 60.0\,\mu$C, $Q_{20} = 120\,\mu$C (d) $U_{10} = 180\,\mu$J, $U_{20} = 360\,\mu$J

30 (a) 6.67 μF (b) 40.0 μC (c) $V_{10} = 4.00$ V, $V_{20} = 2.00$ V (d) $U_{10} = 80.0\,\mu$J, $U_{20} = 40.0\,\mu$J

31 (a) If their capacitance is to be a maximum, the capacitors must be connected in parallel.

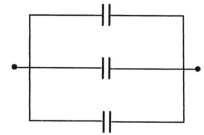

(b)

(1) 1.67 μF

(2) 3.33 μF

(3) 7.50 μF

32 (a) 15.2 μF (b) 2.40 mC, $Q_4 = Q_{15} = 0.632$ mC (c) $V_4 = 158$ V, $V_{15} = 42$ V
(d) $U_4 = 49.9$ mJ, $U_{15} = 13.3$ mJ, $U_{12} = 240$ mJ (e) 303 mJ, 303 mJ

34 (a) 0.242 μF (b) $Q_{1.00} = 1.9\,\mu$C, $Q_{0.250} = 0.48\,\mu$C,
$Q_{0.300} = 2.42\,\mu$C (c) $V_{0.300} = 8.06$ V, $V_{1.00} = V_{0.250} = 1.9$ V (d) 12.1 μJ

35 (a) $2C_0$ (b) $11C_0$

36 Place four of the capacitors in series. Then, the potential across each is 100 V when the potential across the combination is 400 V. The equivalent capacitance of the series combination is 0.500 μF. If we place four such series combinations in parallel, as shown in the circuit diagram, the total capacitance between the terminals is 2.00 μF.

37 0.571 μF, 0.667 μF, 0.800 μF, 0.857 μF, 1.33 μF, 1.43 μF, 1.71 μF, 2.33 μF, 2.80 μF , 3.00 μF, 4.67 μF, 5.00 μF, 6.00 μF, 7.00 μF

38 0.618C

39 (a) 4.80 kV (b) 9.60 mC

40 (a) 40.0 V (b) 4.24 m

41 (a) 7.9 m^2 (b) 23 V (c) 37 μJ (d) 0.16 J

42 (a) 0.333 mm (b) 3.76 m^2

43 (a) 1.55 pF (b) 15.5 nC/m

44 (a) $E_R = \dfrac{2kQ}{RL}$, $u = \dfrac{2k^2 \epsilon_0 Q^2}{R^2 L^2}$ $R_1 \le r \le R_2$

(b) $dU = \dfrac{kQ^2}{RL} dR$ (c) $U = \dfrac{kQ^2}{L} \ln\left(\dfrac{R_2}{R_1}\right)$

45 179 pF/m

46 $C = \dfrac{\epsilon_0 \left(R_2^2 - R_1^2\right)}{2d}(\theta - \Delta\theta)$

47 $\Delta C = -2\dfrac{P}{Y}C$

48 (a) 0.709 mF (b) 829 $\times 10^3$ e/cm^2

50 (a) $E_r = \dfrac{kQ}{r^2}$, $u = \dfrac{k^2 \epsilon_0 Q^2}{2r^4}$ $R_1 \le r \le R_2$

  (b) $dU = \dfrac{kQ^2}{2r^2} dr$ (c) $U = \dfrac{1}{2} Q^2 \left(\dfrac{R_2 - R_1}{4\pi \epsilon_0 R_1 R_2} \right)$

51 $R' = 2R$

52 4.00 μF

53 (a) $V_{100} = V_{400} = 1.20$ kV (b) 640 μJ

54 (a) $V_{4,00} = V_{12.0} = 4.50$ V (b) $U_i = 216$ μJ, $U_f = 162$ μJ

55 (a) 2.4 μF (b) 0.4 mJ

56 (a) 4.0 μF (b) 24 J

57 (a) $V_{4.00} = V_{12.0} = 6.0$ V (b) $U_i = 1.15$ mJ, $U_f = 0.29$ mJ

58 (a) $Q_{50} = 58$ nC, $Q_{20} = 23$ nC (b) $U_i = 90$ μJ, $U_f = 26$ μJ. The stored energy decreases when the two capacitors are connected.

59 (a) $V_1 = V_2 = V_3 = 200$ V (b) $Q_1 = -255$ μC, $Q_2 = 145$ μC, $Q_3 = 545$ μC
  (c) $V_1 = -127$ V, $V_2 = 36.4$ V, $V_3 = 90.9$ V

60 $U' = \frac{1}{2} U$. The missing energy was converted into thermal energy by the resistance of the connecting wires.

61 2.72 nF

62 (a) 1.73 kV (b) 24.0 nC/m

63 (a) 50 μm (b) 240 cm^2

64 $C_{eq} = \left(\dfrac{4\kappa_1 \kappa_2}{3\kappa_1 + \kappa_2} \right) C_0$

65 $Q_1 = \dfrac{2Q}{1 + \kappa}$, $Q_2 = \dfrac{2Q\kappa}{1 + \kappa}$

66 $\quad C_{eq} = \left(\dfrac{\kappa d}{\kappa(d-t)+t} \right) C_0$

67 $\quad$ (a) 16.7 nF (b) 1.17 nC

68 $\quad$ (a) 5.0 (b) 1.3 (c) 50

69 $\quad$ (a) 2.1 (b) 45 cm^2 (c) 5.2 nC

70 $\quad C = \left(\kappa_3 + \dfrac{2\kappa_1\kappa_2}{\kappa_1 + \kappa_2} \right) \left(\dfrac{\epsilon_0 A}{2d} \right)$

71 $\quad$ A series combination of two of the capacitors connected in parallel with a series combination of the other two capacitors will result in total energy U_0 stored in all four capacitors.

72 $\quad$ (a) 14.00 μF (b) 1.14 μF

73 $\quad$ 2.00 μF

74 $\quad$ 1.00 mm

75 $\quad$ (a) $\frac{2}{3}C_0$ (b) C_0 (c) $3C_0$

76 $\quad C_2 C_3 = C_1 C_4$

77 $\quad$ (a) $C_{new} = \dfrac{\epsilon_0 A}{3d}$ (b) $V_{new} = 3V$ (c) $U_{new} = \dfrac{3\epsilon_0 AV^2}{2d}$ (d) $W = \dfrac{\epsilon_0 AV^2}{d}$

78 $\quad C' = \dfrac{\kappa}{\kappa-1} C_0$

79 $\quad$ 133 μC, 267 μC

80 $\quad$ (a) $E_1 = \dfrac{Q}{\kappa_1 \epsilon_0 A}$, $E_2 = \dfrac{Q}{\kappa_2 \epsilon_0 A}$ (b) $V = \dfrac{Qd}{2\epsilon_0 A} \left(\dfrac{1}{\kappa_1} + \dfrac{1}{\kappa_2} \right)$

83 $\quad$ (a) $U = \dfrac{Q^2}{2\epsilon_0 A} x$ (b) $dU = \dfrac{Q^2}{2\epsilon_0 A} dx$

84 (a) $C(x) = \dfrac{\epsilon_0 b}{d}\left[a + (\kappa - 1)x\right]$

85 (a) $U = \dfrac{Q^2 d}{2\epsilon_0 a\left[(\kappa - 1)x + a\right]}$ (b) $F = \dfrac{(\kappa - 1)Q^2 d}{2a\epsilon_0 \left[(\kappa - 1)x + a\right]^2}$ (c)

$F = \dfrac{(\kappa - 1)a\epsilon_0 V^2}{2d}$ (d) The force originates from the fringing fields around the edges of the capacitor. The effect of the force is to pull the polarized dielectric into the space between the capacitor plates.

86 (a) $E_1 = \dfrac{kQ}{\kappa_1 r^2}$, $E_2 = \dfrac{kQ}{\kappa_2 r^2}$ (b) $V = \dfrac{kQ(b-a)}{a+b}\dfrac{\kappa_1 a + \kappa_2 b}{\kappa_1 \kappa_2 ab}$

(c) $C = \dfrac{\kappa_1 \kappa_2 ab(a+b)}{k(b-a)(\kappa_1 a + \kappa_2 b)}$

87 (a) First, show that F is inversely proportional to d for a given V_0. Because F increases as d decreases, a decrease in plate separation will unbalance the system. Hence, the balance is unstable. (b) $V_0 = d_0 \sqrt{\dfrac{2Mg}{\epsilon_0 A}}$

88 (a) $2.51 \times 10^3\ \text{m}^3$ (b) $5.02 \times 10^{-2}\ \text{m}^3$

89 (a) $Q_1 = (200\,\text{V})C_1$, $Q_2 = (200\,\text{V})\kappa C_1$ (b) $U = (2.00 \times 10^4\ \text{V}^2)(1 + \kappa)C_1$
(c) $U_f = (1.00 \times 10^4\ \text{V}^2)C_1(1 + \kappa)^2$ (d) $V_f = 100(1 + \kappa)\,\text{V}$

90 (a) $V = \dfrac{2kQ\ln(b/a)}{\kappa L}$ (b) $\sigma_f(a) = \dfrac{Q}{2\pi aL}$, $\sigma_f(b) = \dfrac{-Q}{2\pi bL}$ (c)

$\sigma_b(a) = \dfrac{-Q(\kappa - 1)}{2\pi aL\kappa}$, $\sigma_b(b) = \dfrac{Q(\kappa - 1)}{2\pi bL\kappa}$ (d) $U - \dfrac{kQ^2 \ln(b/a)}{\kappa L}$ (e)

$W = \dfrac{kQ^2(\kappa - 1)\ln(b/a)}{\kappa L}$

91 $0.100\ \mu\text{F}$, $16.0\ \mu\text{C}$

92 (a) The potential difference between the plates is the same for both halves (the plates are equipotential surfaces). Therefore, $E = V/d$ must be the same everywhere between the plates.

93 $\quad C = \dfrac{\epsilon_0\, ab}{y_0} \ln(2)$

94 $\quad$ (a) $C(V) = C_0 \left(1 + \dfrac{\kappa\, \epsilon_0\, V^2}{2Yd^2} \right)$ (b) 7.97 kV

Chapter 25
Electric Current and Direct-Current Circuits

1   In earlier chapters, the conductors are constrained to be in electrostatic
     equilibrium. In this chapter, this constraint is no longer in place.

2   The analog is a wind-up water pump that pumps water through a tube with a
     necked-down section. One end of the tube is connected to the output port of
     the pump, and the other end of the tube is connected to the input port of the
     pump. The pump, including the spring, is analogous to the battery. The tube
     is analogous to the wires. The necked-down section is analogous to the
     resistor.

3   (c)

4   (a)

5   (a)

6   The longer the wire is, the higher its resistance is. Thus, the longer the
     wire is, the smaller the current in the wire is. The smaller the current is,
     the smaller the drift speed of the charge carriers is. The claim that the drift
     speed is independent of length is bogus.

7   No, it is not necessarily true for a battery. Under normal operating
     conditions, the current in the battery is in the direction away from the
     negative battery terminal and toward the positive battery terminal. That is, it
     is opposite to the direction of the electric field.

8   An emf is a source of energy that gives rise to a potential difference between
     two points and may result in current flow if there is a conducting path,
     whereas a potential difference is the consequence of two points in space
     being at different potentials.

9   (e)

10   (b)

11   (d)

12   (c)

13 You should decrease the resistance. The heat output is given by $P = V^2/R$. Because the voltage across the resistor is constant, decreasing the resistance will increase P.

14 (*b*)

15 (*a*)

16 (*b*)

17 (*a*)

18 (*a*)

19 (*a*) False (*b*) True (*c*) True

20 Because of the voltmeter's high resistance, if you connect a voltmeter in series with a circuit element the, current, both in the voltmeter and in the rest of the circuit, will be very small. This means that there is little chance of heating the voltmeter and causing damage. However, because of the ammeter's low resistance, if you connect an ammeter in parallel with a circuit element, the current, both in the ammeter and in the entire circuit, excluding and elements in parallel with the ammeter, will be very large. This means that there is a good chance of overheating and causing damage, maybe even a fire. For this reason, ammeters are often equipped with fuses or circuit breakers.

21 (*b*)

22 $\frac{1}{2}T$

23 $P_2 = \frac{1}{2} P$ and $P_3 = \frac{1}{2} P$

24 (*b*)

25 1.9 kA

26 (*a*) 5.1 mΩ (*b*) 0.46 V (*c*) 41.3 W

27 26 m

28 $127

29 12 gauge

30   (*a*) 3.2 mA (*b*) 3.7 mW, 123%P_{quoted} (*c*) 12.5 h

31   0.28 mm/s

32 $I = a\lambda\omega$

33   (*a*) 0.21 mm/s, 0.53 mm/s (*b*) 0.396

34   (*a*) 3.2×10^{-3} mm^{-3} (*b*) 3.7×10^{17} (*c*) 0.32 kA/m^2

35   (*a*) 1.04×10^{8} m^{-1} (*b*) 1.04×10^{14} m^{-3} (*c*) 5.00 kA/m^2

36 3.9×10^{5} m/s

37   0.86 s

38   (*a*) 1.0 V (*b*) 0.10 V/m

39   (*a*) 33.3 Ω (*b*) 0.750 A

40   (*a*) 42 mΩ (*b*) 0.20 kA

41   1.9 V

42   (*a*) 1.5 km (*b*) 10.0 A

43   63 light-years

44   (*a*) $V_{Cu} = 3.5$ V, $V_{Fe} = 12$ V (*b*) $E_{Cu} = 43$ mV/m, $E_{Fe} = 0.25$ V/m

45   1.20 Ω

46   (*a*) 0.32 Ω (*b*) 97 mV/m (*c*) 2.38×10^{5} s = 2.75 d

47   31 mΩ

48 $R = \dfrac{\rho\pi}{t\ln(b/a)}$

49 $R = \dfrac{\rho L}{\pi ab}$

50   130 $\mu\Omega$

51   (*a*) $R = \dfrac{\rho}{2\pi L}\ln(b/a)$ (*b*) 2.05 A

52   (*a*) 28 mΩ (*b*) 30 mΩ

53   46°C

54 6×10^{2}°C

55   (*a*) 15.0 A (*b*) 11.1 Ω (*c*) 1.30 kW

56   (*a*) 30 mΩ (*b*) 0.30% (*c*) 8°C

57   (*b*) 3×10^{2}

58   (*a*) 0.25 kΩ (*b*) 14.0 μm

59   (*a*) 636 K (*b*) As the filament heats up, its resistance decreases. This results in more power being dissipated, further heat, higher temperature, etc. If not controlled, this thermal runaway can burn out the filament.

60   (*a*) 57.6 Ω, 4.17 A (*b*) 250 W

61   0.18 kJ

62   0.03 Ω

63   (*a*) 0.24 kW (*b*) 0.23 kW (*c*) 1.7 kJ (*d*) 84 J

64   (*a*) 20 A, 0 W (*b*) 1.1 A, 6.4 W (*c*) 0.58 A, 3.4 W (*d*) 0 A, 0 W

65   (*a*) 6.9 MJ (*b*) 12.8 h

66   (*a*) 116 V (*b*) 15

67   (*a*) 26.7 kW (*b*) 576 kC (*c*) 69.1 MJ (*d*) 57.6 km (*e*) \$0.03/km

68   (*a*) 0.833 A, 144 Ω (*c*) 91.7 W. The power calculated using the approximation is 0.1 percent less than the power calculated exactly.

69 $I_4 = 3.00$ A, $I_3 = 4.00$ A, $I_6 = 2.00$ A

70 $I_2 = 2.00$ A, $I_3 = 2.67$ A, $I_6 = 0.667$ A

71 (b) It would not affect it.

72 (a) $I_3 = 1.58$ A, $I_2 = 0.632$ A, $I_4 = 0.316$ A (b) 9.47 W

73 0.45 kΩ

74 (a) 3.00 V (b) 1.00 Ω

75 (a) 6.00 Ω (b) The current in both the 6.00-Ω and the 12.0-Ω resistor in the upper branch is 667 mA. The current in each 6.00-Ω resistor in the parallel combination in the lower branch is 667 mA. The current in the 6.00-Ω resistor on the right in the lower branch is 1.33 A.

76 (a) 4.10 Ω (b) The current through the 6.00-Ω resistor is 1.43 A, the current through the lower 4.00-Ω resistor is 1.50 A, the current through the 4.00-Ω resistor that is in parallel with the 2.00-Ω and 4.00-Ω resistors is 0.86 A, the current through the 2.00-Ω and 4.00-Ω resistors that are in series is 0.57 A, and the currents through the two 8.00-Ω resistors are 0.75 A.

77 8 pieces

78 11.3 Ω

79 (a) $R_3 = \dfrac{R_1^2}{R_1 + R_2}$ (b) 0 (c) $R_1 = \dfrac{R_3 + \sqrt{R_3^2 + 4R_2 R_3}}{2}$

80 (a) $R_3 = 1.60$ Ω, $R_{ab} = 4.00$ Ω (b) $R_2 = 0$, $R_{ab} = 3.00$ Ω (c) $R_1 = 6.00$ Ω, $R_{ab} = 6.00$ Ω

81 (a) 4.00 A (b) 2.00 V (c) 1.00 Ω

82 (a) 1.0 A (b) $P_{12} = 12$ W, $P_6 = -6.0$ W (c) $P_2 = 2.0$ W, $P_4 = 4.0$ W

83

(a)

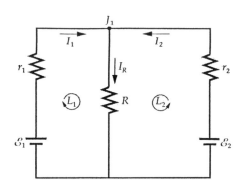

(b) $I_1 = -19.0$ A, $I_2 = 25.1$ A, $I_R = 6.17$ A (c) Battery 2 supplies 311 W. O the 234 W that is delivered to battery 1, 216 W goes into recharging battery 1 and 18.0 W is dissipated by the internal resistance. In addition, 76.2 W is delivered to the 2.00-Ω resistor.

84 600 Ω

85 (a) $I_{4\Omega} = 0.667$ A, $I_{3\Omega} = 0.889$ A, $I_{6\Omega} = 1.56$ A (b) $V_{ab} = 9.33$ V
(c) $P_{\text{left}} = 8.00$ W, $P_{\text{right}} = 10.7$ W

86 (a) $I_{2\Omega} = 3.00$ A, $I_{3\Omega} = 2.00$ A, $I_{1\Omega} = 1.00$A (b) $V_{ab} = 1.00$ V
(c) $P_{7V} = 21.0$ W, $P_{5V} = 10.0$ W

87 For the series combination, the power delivered to the load is greater if $R > r$ and is greatest when $R = 2r$. If $R = r$, both arrangements provide the same power to the load. For the parallel combination, the power delivered to the load is greater if $R < r$ and is a maximum when $R = \frac{1}{2} r$.

88 (b) 45 kΩ

89 $V_a - V_b = 2.40$ V

90 (a) $I_{1\ 2\Omega} = 2.00$ A, $I_{2\Omega} = -1.00$ A, , $I_{6\Omega} = 1.00$ A (b) $P_{8V} = 16.0$ W ,
$P_{4V} = -4.00$ W (c) $P_{1\Omega} = 4.00$ W, $P_{2\Omega,\text{ left}} = 8.00$ W, $P_{2\Omega,\text{ middle}} = 2.00$ W,
$P_{6\Omega} = 6.00$ W

91 (a) 3.33 V (b) 3.33 V (c) 3.13 V (d) 2.00 V (e) 0.435 V
(f) $R_{\text{max}} = 1.67$ MΩ

92 5.00 kΩ

93 2.5 Ω

94 195 kΩ

95 (*a*) 600 μC (*b*) 0.200 A (*c*) 3.00 ms (*d*) 81.2 μC

96 (*a*) 30.0 mJ
(*c*)

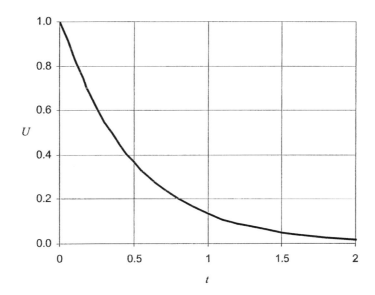

97 2.18 MΩ

98 48.1 MΩ

99 (*a*) 5.69 μC (*b*) 1.10 μC/s (*c*) 1.10 μA (*d*) 6.62 μW (*e*) 2.44 μW (*f*) 4.19μW

100 (*a*) 25.0 A (*b*) $R_1 = 0.400$ Ω, $R_2 = 10.0$ Ω, $R_3 = 6.67$ Ω

102 (*a*) 3.42 A (*b*) 0.962 A (*c*) $Q_{10\,\mu F} = 260\ \mu$C, $Q_{5\,\mu F} = 130\ \mu$C

103 (*a*) 0.250 A (*b*) 62.5 mA (*c*) $I_2(t) = (62.5\,\text{mA})\left(1 - e^{-t/0.750\,\text{ms}}\right)$

104 (*a*) 41.7 μA (*b*) 27.8 μA (*c*) $I(t) = (27.8\,\mu\text{A})e^{-t/1.50\,\text{s}}$

105 (*a*) 48.0 μA (*b*) 0.866 s

106 (*a*) 96.0 μA (*b*) 1.73 s

107 (a) (1) The potential drops across R_2 and R_3 are equal, so $I_2 > I_3$. The current in R_1 equals the sum of the currents in I_2 and I_3, so I_1 is greater than either I_2 or I_3. (b) $I_1 = 1.50$ A, $I_2 = 1.00$ A, $I_3 = 0.50$ A

108 (a) The 25-W bulb will be brighter. The more power delivered to a bulb the brighter the bulb. The resistance of the 25-W bulb is 4 times greater than that of the 100-W bulb, and in the series combination, the same current I exists through the bulbs. Hence, $I^2 R_{25} > I^2 R_{100}$. (b) $P_{25} = 16$ W, $P_{100} = 4$ W

109 (a) 43.9 Ω (b) 300 Ω (c) 3.8 kΩ

110 (a) 9.8 kΩ (b) $\Delta R_x / R_x = 10\%$ (c) For $L_1 = 50.0$ cm, $L_2 = 50.0$ cm, $R_0 = R_x = 9.8$ kΩ. Hence, a resistor of approximately 10 kΩ will cause the bridge to balance near the 50.0-cm mark.

111 (a) $2.18 \times 10^{13} /$ s (b) 210 J/s (c) 27.6 s

112 (a) 50.0 mA (b) 5.00 kW

113 0.16 L/s

114 (c) 2.5 h

115 (a) 10.0 ms (c) 1.00 GΩ (d) 60.9 ps (e) 2.89 kW

116

(a)

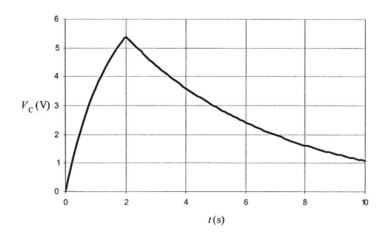

(b) $V_C (2.00\,\text{s}) = 5.38\,\text{V}$, $V_C (8.00\,\text{s}) = 1.62\,\text{V}$

118 (a) $\dfrac{U_i}{U_f} = 1 + \dfrac{C_2}{C_1}$ (b) $I(t) = \dfrac{V_0}{R} e^{-t/\tau}$, where $\tau = R \dfrac{C_1 C_2}{C_1 + C_2}$ (c) $P(t) = \dfrac{V_0^2}{R} e^{-2t/\tau}$

where $\tau = R \dfrac{C_1 C_2}{C_1 + C_2}$ (d) $E = \dfrac{1}{2} \dfrac{C_1 C_2}{C_1 + C_2} V_0^2$. This energy, dissipated as Joule

heating in the resistor, is exactly the difference between the initial and final
energies found in part (a).

119 (a) $R_{eq} = \left(\dfrac{1 + \sqrt{5}}{2} \right) R$ (b) $R_{eq} = \dfrac{R_1 + \sqrt{R_1^2 + 4 R_1 R_2}}{2}$

120

(a)

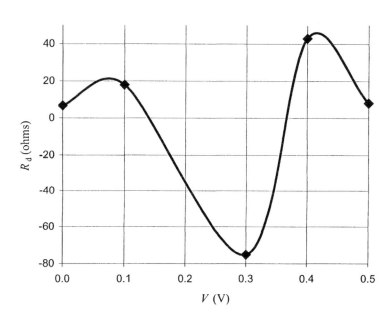

(b) The differential resistance becomes negative at approximately 0.14 V.
(c) The maximum differential resistance for this diode is approximately
45 Ω and occurs at about 0.42 V. (d) The diode exhibits no resistance where
the curve crosses the V axis; that is, at $V = 0.14$ V and 0.36 V.

Chapter 26
The Magnetic Field

1   (*b*)

2   The direction of the force depends on the direction of the velocity. We do not define the direction of the magnetic field to be in the direction of the force because, if we did, the magnetic field would be in a different direction each time the velocity was in a different direction. If this were the case, the magnetic field would not be a useful construct.

3   Because the alternating current running through the filament is changing direction every 1/60 s, the filament experiences a force that changes direction at the frequency of the current. Thus, it oscillates at 60 Hz.

5   (*a*)

6   (*c*)

8

Similarities	Differences
1. Their density on a surface perpendicular to the lines is a measure of the strength of the field.	1. Magnetic field lines neither begin nor end. Electric field lines begin on positive charges and end on negative charges.
2. The lines point in the direction of the field.	2. Electric forces are parallel or anti-parallel to the field lines. Magnetic forces are perpendicular to the field lines.
3. The lines do not cross.	

9   (*a*) False (*b*) True (*c*) True (*d*) False

11   According to the principle of relativity, this is equivalent to the electron moving from right to left at speed *v* with the magnet stationary. When the electron is directly over the magnet, the field points directly up, so there is a force directed out of the page on the electron.

12   1 mN/m

13 $I \sim 2 \times 10^3$. You should advise him to develop some other act. A current of 2000 A would overheat the wire (which is a gross understatement).

14 $\vec{F} = -(0.125\,\mathrm{pN})\hat{j}$

15 (a) $-(3.8\,\mu\mathrm{N})\hat{k}$ (b) $-(7.5\,\mu\mathrm{N})\hat{k}$ (c) 0 (d) $(7.5\,\mu\mathrm{N})\hat{j}$

16 (a) $-(6.4\times10^{-16}\,\mathrm{N})\hat{j}$ (b) $(8.8\times10^{-16}\,\mathrm{N})$ (c) 0
(d) $(7.1\times10^{-16}\,\mathrm{N})\hat{i} - (9.5\times10^{-16}\,\mathrm{N})\hat{j}$

17 0.96 N

18 $-(0.14\,\mathrm{N})\hat{k}$

19 $-(19\,\mathrm{fN})\hat{i} - (13\,\mathrm{fN})\hat{j} - (58\,\mathrm{fN})\hat{k}$

20 $(86\,\mathrm{mN})\hat{i} - (65\,\mathrm{mN})\hat{j}$

21 1.5 A

22 (a) $4.7° = 82$ mrad (b) 2.0 mrad/mT = 2.0 rad/T

23 $(10\,\mathrm{T})\hat{i} + (10\,\mathrm{T})\hat{j} - (15\,\mathrm{T})\hat{k}$

24 $(0.50\,\mathrm{T})\hat{i} + (0.50\,\mathrm{T})\hat{j}$

27 (a) 87 ns (b) 4.7×10^{7} m/s (c) 11 MeV

28 (a) 0.70 mm (b) 0.11 ns, 9.1 GHz

29 (a) $2v_{\alpha} = 2v_{\mathrm{d}} = 1v_{\mathrm{p}}$ (b) $1K_{\alpha} = 2K_{\mathrm{d}} = 1K_{\mathrm{p}}$ (c) $L_{\alpha} = 2L_{\mathrm{d}} = 2L_{\mathrm{p}}$

32 60°, 13.1 mm

33 (a) 24°, 1.3×10^{6} m/s (b) 24°, 6.3×10^{5} m/s

34 6.64×10^{3} y

35 (a) 1.6×10^{6} m/s (b) 14 keV (c) 7.7 eV

36 (a) $-(11\,\text{kV/m})\hat{k}$ (b) Because both $\vec{F}_{\text{mag}}$ and $\vec{F}_{\text{elec}}$ would be reversed, electrons are not deflected either.

37 7.37 mm

38 0.12 MV

39 (a) 63.3 cm (b) 2.58 cm

40 18 cm

41 $\Delta t_{58} = 15.7\,\mu\text{s}$, $\Delta t_{60} = 16.3\,\mu\text{s}$

42 (a) 1.9×10^5 m/s (b) 1 cm

43 (a) 21 MHz (b) 46 MeV (c) $f_{\text{deuterons}} = 11\,\text{MHz}$, $K_{\text{deuterons}} = 23\,\text{MeV}$

44 (a) 27 MHz (b) 40 cm (c) 2.5×10^2 rev

47 (a) $0.30\,\text{A} \cdot \text{m}^2$ (b) $0.13\,\text{N} \cdot \text{m}$

48 $28\,\mu\text{N} \cdot \text{m}$

49 (a) 0 (b) $2.7 \times 10^{-3}\,\text{N} \cdot \text{m}$

50 (a) 0 (b) $2.1 \times 10^{-3}\,\text{N} \cdot \text{m}$

51 $B_{\text{min}} = \dfrac{mg}{I\pi R}$

52 (a) 37° (b) $\hat{n} = 0.80\hat{i} - 0.60\hat{j}$ (c) $\vec{\mu} = (0.34\,\text{A} \cdot \text{m}^2)\hat{i} - (0.25\,\text{A} \cdot \text{m}^2)\hat{j}$
(d) $\vec{\tau} = (0.50\,\text{N} \cdot \text{m})\hat{k}$ (e) 0.38 J

53 (a) $(0.84\,\text{N} \cdot \text{m})\hat{k}$ (b) 0 (c) 0 (d) $(0.59\,\text{N} \cdot \text{m})\hat{k}$

54 (a) $2.9\,\text{A} \cdot \text{m}^2$ (b) $-58\,\text{mJ}$

55 $0.38\,\text{A} \cdot \text{m}^2$, into the page

58 $\bar{\mu} = \frac{1}{4}L\rho\pi\left(R_0^4 - R_i^4\right)\vec{\omega}$

61 $\mu = \frac{4}{3}\pi\sigma R^4\omega$

62 $\mu = \frac{4}{15}\pi\rho R^5\omega$

63 (a) $\tau = \frac{1}{4}\pi\sigma r^4\omega B\sin\theta$ (b) $\Omega = \dfrac{\pi\sigma r^2 B}{2m}\sin\theta$

64 (a) 0.107 mm/s (b) 5.85×10^{28} m^{-3} (c) $V_a > V_b$ (The Hall effect electric field is directed from a toward b.)

65 (a) 3.68×10^{-5} m/s (b) $1.47\,\mu$V

66 (a) 1.36 T(b) 3.56 T (c) 5.43 T

67 1.0 mV

69 4

70 $(8.78\,\text{N/m})\hat{k}$

71 (a) 1.3 μs (b) 2.4×10^6 m/s (c) 0.12 MeV

74 (b) Toward the right

75 (a) $B = -\dfrac{mg}{IL}\tan\theta$ (b) $\vec{a} = g\sin\theta$, up the incline

77 (a) $(10\,\text{V/m})\hat{j}$ (b) The positive end has the lesser y coordinate. (c) 20 V

78 $T = \sqrt{2\pi m/(IB)}$

80 $R_d/R_p = \sqrt{2}$, $R_\alpha/R_p = 1$

81 1.0×10^{-28} kg

Chapter 27
Sources of the Magnetic Field

1 Note that, while the two far fields (the fields far from the dipoles) are the same, the two near fields (the fields near to the dipoles) are not. At the center of the electric dipole, the electric field is antiparallel to the direction of the far field above and below the dipole, and at the center of the magnetic dipole, the magnetic field is parallel to the direction of the far field above and below the dipole. It is especially important to note that while the electric field lines begin and terminate on electric charges, the magnetic field lines are continuous, i.e., they form closed loops.

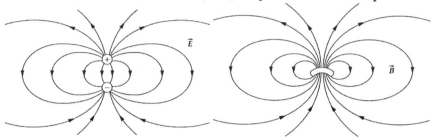

2 (*c*)

3 (*a*)

4 (*a*)

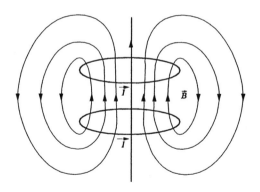

(*b*)

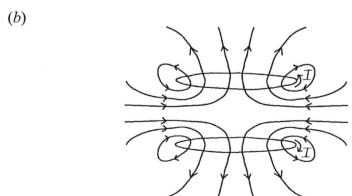

5   Both tell you about the respective fluxes through closed surfaces. In the electrical case, the flux is proportional to the net charge enclosed. In the magnetic case, the flux is always zero because there is no such thing as magnetic charge (a magnetic monopole). The source of the magnetic field is NOT the equivalent of electric charge; that is, it is NOT a thing called magnetic charge, but rather it is moving electric charges.

6   Gauss's law for magnetism now reads: "The flux of the magnetic field through any closed surface is equal to zero." Just like each electric pole has an electric pole strength (an amount of electric charge), each magnetic pole would have a magnetic pole strength (an amount of magnetic charge). Gauss's law for magnetism would read: "The flux of the magnetic field through any closed surface is proportional to the total amount of magnetic charge inside."

7   Clockwise

8   The coils attract each other and tend to move closer together when there is current in the spring. The current elements in the same direction will attract each other, and a current element of one segment of a coil are close to the current elements in adjacent coils that are in the same direction as it is.

9   (a) True (b) False (c) True (d) True

10   (a)

11   H_2, CO_2, and N_2 are diamagnetic ($\chi_m < 0$); O_2 is paramagnetic ($\chi_m > 0$).

12   It will tend to form a circle. Oppositely directed current elements will repel each other, and so opposite sides of the loop will repel.

13   (a) $\vec{B}(0,0) = -(9.0\,\text{pT})\hat{k}$ (b $\vec{B}(0,1.0\,\text{m}) = -(36\,\text{pT})\hat{k}$ (c) $\vec{B}(0,3.0\,\text{m}) = (36\,\text{pT})\hat{k}$
        (d) $\vec{B}(0,4.0\,\text{m}) = (9.0\,\text{pT})\hat{k}$

14   (a) $\vec{B}(1.0\,\text{m},3.0\,\text{m}) = (13\,\text{pT})\hat{k}$ (b) $\vec{B}(2.0\,\text{m},2.0\,\text{m}) = 0$
        (c) $\vec{B}(2.0\,\text{m},3.0\,\text{m}) = (3.2\,\text{pT})\hat{k}$

15   (a) $\vec{B}(2.0\,\text{m},2.0\,\text{m}) = 0$ (b) $\vec{B}(6.0\,\text{m},4.0\,\text{m}) = -(3.6 \times 10^{-23}\,\text{T})\hat{k}$
        (c) $\vec{B}(3.0\,\text{m},6.0\,\text{m}) = (4.0 \times 10^{-23}\,\text{T})\hat{k}$

16   12.5 T

17 $\epsilon_0 \, \mu_0 v^2$

18   (a) $d\vec{B}(3.0\,\text{m},0,0) = (44\,\text{pT})\hat{j}$ (b) $d\vec{B}(-6.0\,\text{m},0,0) = -(11\,\text{pT})\hat{j}$
     (c) $d\vec{B}(0,0,3.0\,\text{m}) = 0$ (d) $d\vec{B}(0,3.0\,\text{m},0) = -(44\,\text{pT})\hat{i}$

19 $d\vec{B}(0,3.0\,\text{m},4.0\,\text{m}) = -(9.6\,\text{pT})\hat{i}$

20   (a) $B(2.0\,\text{m},4.0\,\text{m},0) = 20\text{ pT}$

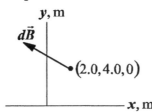

     (b) $B(2.0\,\text{m},0,4.0\,\text{m}) = 8.9\,\text{pT}$

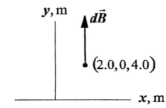

21   (a) $B(0) = 54\,\mu\text{T}$ (b) $B(0.010\,\text{m}) = 46\,\mu\text{T}$ (c) $B(0.020\,\text{m}) = 31\,\mu\text{T}$
     (d) $B(0.35\,\text{m}) = 34\,\text{nT}$

22   The spreadsheet solution is shown below. The formulas used to calculate the quantities in the columns are as follows:

Cell	Formula/Content	Algebraic Form
B1	1.13×10^{-7}	μ_0
B2	0.30	r
B3	250	N
B3	15	I
B5	0.5*\$B\$1*\$B\$3*(\$B\$2^2)*\$B\$4	$\text{Coeff} = \dfrac{\mu_0 N r^2 I}{2}$
A8	-0.30	$-r$
B8	\$B\$5*((\$B\$2/2+A8)^2+\$B\$2^2)^(−3/2)	$\dfrac{\mu_0 N r^2 I}{2}\left[\left(\dfrac{r}{2}+z\right)^2+r^2\right]^{-3/2}$
C8	\$B\$5* ((\$B\$2/2−A8)^2+\$B\$2^2)^(−3/2)	$\dfrac{\mu_0 N r^2 I}{2}\left[\left(\dfrac{r}{2}-z\right)^2+r^2\right]^{-3/2}$
D8	10^4(B8+C8)	$B_x = 10^4(B_1 + B_2)$

	A	B	C	D
1	μ_0-	1.26E-06	N/A^2	
2	$r=$	0.30	m	
3	$N=$	250	turns	
4	$I=$	15	A	
5	Coeff=	2.13E−04		
6				
7	z	B_1	B_2	$B(z)$
8	−0.30	5.63E−03	1.34E−03	70
9	−0.29	5.86E−03	1.41E−03	73
67	0.29	1.41E−03	5.86E−03	73
68	0.30	1.34E−03	5.63E−03	70

The following graph of B_z as a function of z was plotted using the data in the preceding table.

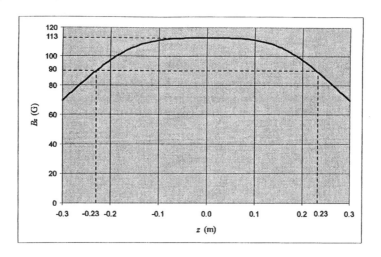

The maximum value of B_z is 113 G. Eighty percent of this maximum value is 90 G. We see that the field is within 20 percent of 113 G in the interval $\boxed{-0.23\,\text{m} < z < 0.23\,\text{m}}$.

24

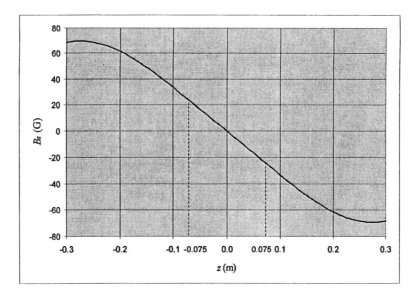

Inspection of the table reveals that the slope of the graph of B_z, evaluated at $z = 0$, is −337 G. One percent of this value corresponds approximately to -0.075 m $< z < 0.075$ m, or $\boxed{-0.25R < z < 0.25R}$.

25 (a) $\vec{B}(-3.0\,\text{cm}) = -(89\,\mu\text{T})\hat{k}$ (b) $\vec{B}(0) = 0$ (c) $\vec{B}(3.0\,\text{cm}) = (89\,\mu\text{T})\hat{k}$
(d) $\vec{B}(9.0\,\text{cm}) = -(160\,\mu\text{T})\hat{k}$

26

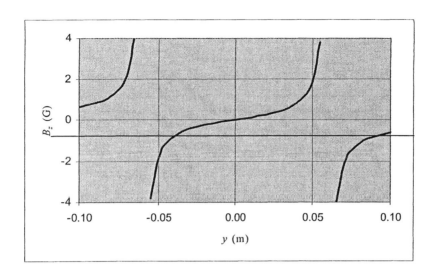

27 (*a*) $\vec{B}(-3.0\,\text{cm}) = -(0.18\,\text{mT})\hat{k}$ (*b*) $\vec{B}(0) = -(0.13\,\text{mT})\hat{k}$
(*c*) $\vec{B}(3.0\,\text{cm}) = -(0.18\,\text{mT})\hat{k}$ (*d*) $\vec{B}(9.0\,\text{cm}) = (0.11\,\text{mT})\hat{k}$

28

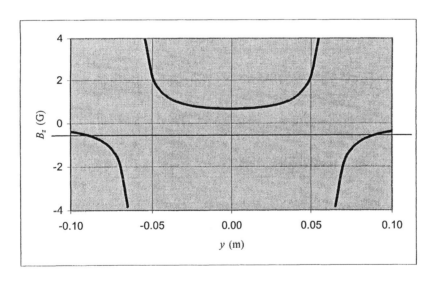

29 (*a*) $\vec{B}(z = 8.0\,\text{cm}) = (48\,\mu\text{T})\hat{j}$ (*b*) $\vec{B}(z = 8.0\,\text{cm}) = -(64\,\mu\text{T})\hat{k}$

30 $0.67\,\text{mN/m}$

31 (*a*) Because the currents repel, they are antiparallel. (*b*) 39 mA

32 0.23 mT, into the page

33 80 A

34 (a) $52\,\mu\text{T}$, toward the right (b) $7.8 \times 10^{-4}\,\text{N/m}$, up the page

35 (a) $30\,\mu\text{T}$, down the page (b) $4.5 \times 10^{-4}\,\text{N/m}$, toward the right

36 $\vec{B} = 0$ everywhere on the plane that contains both the z axis and the line $y = x$ in the $z = 0$ plane.

37 (a) 80 A (b) $\vec{B}(5.0\,\text{cm}) = -(0.24\,\text{mT})\hat{j}$

38 (a) $\vec{B} = \dfrac{3\mu_0 I}{4\pi L}\left[\hat{i} - \hat{j}\right]$ (b) $\vec{B} = \dfrac{\mu_0 I}{4\pi L}\left[\hat{i} - \hat{j}\right]$ (c) $\vec{B} = \dfrac{\mu_0 I}{4\pi L}\left[-\hat{i} - 3\hat{j}\right]$

39 (a) $\dfrac{F}{\ell} = \dfrac{3\sqrt{2}\mu_0 I^2}{4\pi a}$ (b) $\dfrac{F}{\ell} = \dfrac{\sqrt{2}\mu_0 I^2}{4\pi a}$

40 $\vec{B} = \left(1 + \sqrt{2}\right)\dfrac{\mu_0 I}{2\pi R}\,\hat{i}$

41 (a) 3.3 mT (b) 1.6 mT

42 0.70 mT

45 $B_{\text{inside}} = 0$, $B_{\text{outside}} = \dfrac{\mu_0 I}{2\pi R}$. The direction of the magnetic field is in the direction of the curled fingers of your right hand when you grab the cylinder with your right thumb in the direction of the current.

46 (a) $\oint_{C_1}\vec{B}\cdot d\vec{\ell} = -\mu_0(8.0\,\text{A})$, $\oint_{C_2}\vec{B}\cdot d\vec{\ell} = 0$, $\oint_{C_3}\vec{B}\cdot d\vec{\ell} = +\mu_0(8.0\,\text{A})$ (b) None of the paths can be used to find $\vec{B}$.

48 (*a*)

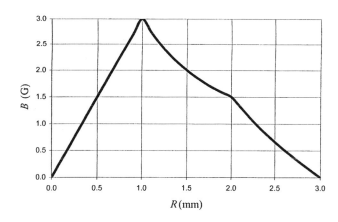

(*b*) $B_{R>R_3} = 0$

49 (*a*) $B_{R<a} = 0$ (*b*) $B_{a<R<b} = \dfrac{\mu_0 I}{2\pi R}\dfrac{R^2 - a^2}{b^2 - a^2}$ (*c*) $B_{R>b} = \dfrac{\mu_0 I}{2\pi R}$

50 $B = \mu_0 n I$

51 (*a*) $B(1.10\,\text{cm}) = 27.3\,\text{mT}$ (*b*) $B(1.50\,\text{cm}) = 20.0\,\text{mT}$

52 (*a*) Because its vertical components cancel at *P*, the magnetic field points to the right (i.e., in the +*y* direction).

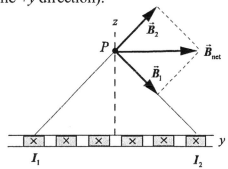

(*b*) The vertical components of the field cancel in pairs. The magnetic field is in the +*y* direction.

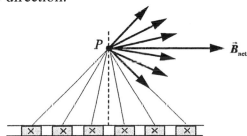

(*c*) The magnetic field is in the +*y* direction. This result follows from the same arguments that were used in (*a*) and (*b*).

(*d*) Below the sheet the magnetic field points to the left (i.e., in the −*y* direction). The vertical components cancel in pairs.

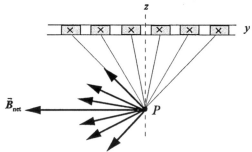

53 (*a*) $B = B_{app} = 10.1\,\text{mT}$ (*b*) $B_{app} = 10.1\,\text{mT}$, $B = 1.5\,\text{T}$

54 (*a*) Because $\chi_{\text{m, tungsten}} > 0$, $B > B_{app}$ and B will decrease when the tungsten core is removed. (*b*) $6.8 \times 10^{-3}\%$

55 -4.0×10^{-5}

56 (*a*) 63 mT (*b*) 63 mT (*c*) 63 mT

57 5.43 A/m

58 (*a*) 0.26 T (*b*) 0.94 T

59

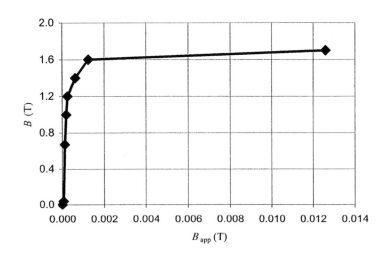

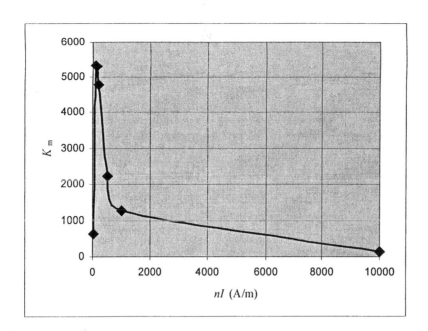

60 $0.587\,\mu_{\mathrm{B}}$

61 $1.69\,\mu_{\mathrm{B}}$

63 (b) 7.46×10^{-4}

64 (a) $M_{\mathrm{S}} = 5.58\times10^{5}\,\mathrm{A/m}$, $B_{\mathrm{S}} = 0.702\,\mathrm{T}$ (b) 5.23×10^{-4} (c) In calculating χ_{m} in part (b), we neglected any diamagnetic effects.

65 $B_{\mathrm{app}} = \dfrac{\mu_0 NI}{2\pi a}$, $B = \dfrac{\mu_0 NI}{2\pi a} + \mu_0 M$

66 (a) 95.5 A/m (b) 30.1 mT (c) 0.398%

67 (a) 30.2 mT (b) 6.96 A/m (c) 30.2 mT

68 0.86 T, $6.9\times10^{5}\,\mathrm{A/m}$

69 11.7, $1.48\times10^{-5}\,\mathrm{N/A^{2}}$

70 11.0 A

71 (a) 12.6 mT (b) $1.36\times10^{6}\,\mathrm{A/m}$ (c) 137

72   (a) 1.26 mT (b) 1.26×10^6 A/m (c) 1.26×10^3

73   (a) 1.42×10^6 A/m (b) $\boldsymbol{K}_m = 90.0$, $\mu = 1.13 \times 10^{-4}$ T·m/A, $\chi_m = 89$

74   0.754 T

75   (a) $(8.00 \, \text{T/m})r$ (b) $\left(3.20 \times 10^{-3} \, \text{T·m}\right)\dfrac{1}{r}$ (c) $\left(8.00 \times 10^{-6} \, \text{T·m}\right)\dfrac{1}{r}$ (d) Note that the field in the ferromagnetic region is that which would be produced in a nonmagnetic region by a current of $400I = 1600$ A. The ampèrian current on the inside of the surface of the ferromagnetic material must therefore be $(1600 - 40)$ A = 1560 A in the direction of I. On the outside surface, there must then be an ampèrian current of 1560 A in the opposite direction.

76 $24 \, \mu$T , out of the page

77 $\vec{\boldsymbol{B}}_P = \dfrac{\mu_0 I}{4}\left(\dfrac{1}{R_1} - \dfrac{1}{R_2}\right)$, out of the page

79 $\vec{\boldsymbol{B}}_P = \dfrac{\mu_0}{2\pi}\dfrac{I}{a}\left(1 + \sqrt{2}\right)$, out of the page

80   If the cable runs in a direction other than east-west, its magnetic field is in a direction different than that of Earth's, and by moving the compass about, one should observe a change in the direction of the compass needle.

 If the cable runs east-west, its magnetic field is in the north-south direction and thus either adds to or subtracts from Earth's field, depending on the current direction and location of the compass. If the magnetic field is toward the north, the two fields add and the resultant field is stronger. If perturbed, the compass needle will oscillate about its equilibrium position. The stronger the field, the higher the frequency of oscillation. By moving from place to place and systematically perturbing the needle, one should be able to detect a change frequency, and thus a change in magnetic field strength.

81   The $+x$ and $+y$ directions are up the page and to the right.
(a) $\vec{\boldsymbol{F}}_{\text{top}} = -\left(2.5 \times 10^{-5} \, \text{N}\right)\hat{\boldsymbol{j}}$, $\vec{\boldsymbol{F}}_{\text{left side}} = \left(1.0 \times 10^{-4} \, \text{N}\right)\hat{\boldsymbol{i}}$,
$\vec{\boldsymbol{F}}_{\text{bottom}} = \left(2.5 \times 10^{-5} \, \text{N}\right)\hat{\boldsymbol{j}}$, $\vec{\boldsymbol{F}}_{\text{right side}} = \left(-0.29 \times 10^{-4} \, \text{N}\right)\hat{\boldsymbol{i}}$
(b) $\vec{\boldsymbol{F}}_{\text{net}} = \left(0.71 \times 10^{-4} \, \text{N}\right)\hat{\boldsymbol{i}}$

82   0.70 μT, into the page

83 7.1 μT, into the page

84 (a) 3.20×10^{-16} N into the page (b) 3.20×10^{-16} N toward the right
(c) 0

85

Cell	Formula/Content	Algebraic Form
B1	1.00E–07	$\dfrac{\mu_0}{4\pi}$
B2	5.00	I
B3	2.55E–03	r_0
C6	10^4*\$B\$1*2*\$B\$2*A6/\$B\$3^2	$\dfrac{\mu_0}{4\pi}\dfrac{2I}{R_0^2}R$
C17	10^4*\$B\$1*2*\$B\$2*A6/A17	$\dfrac{\mu_0}{4\pi}\dfrac{2I}{R}$

	A	B	C
1	$\mu/4\pi=$	1.00E–07	N/A^2
2	$I=$	5	A
3	$R_0=$	2.55E–03	m
4			
5	R (m)	R (mm)	B (T)
6	0.00E+00	0.00E+00	0.00E+00
7	2.55E–04	2.55E–01	3.92E–01
105	2.52E–02	2.52E+01	3.96E–01
106	2.55E–02	2.55E+01	3.92E–01

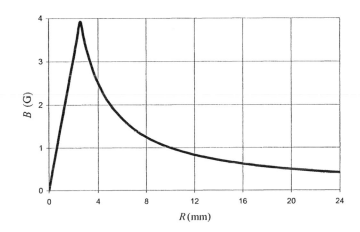

86 $1.97\,\mu\text{N}\cdot\text{m}$

87   (a) $5.24\times10^{-2}\,\text{A}\cdot\text{m}^2$ (b) $7.70\times10^5\,\text{A/m}$ (c) $23.1\,\text{kA}$

89   (a) 15.5 GA (b) Because Earth's magnetic field points down at the north pole, application of the right-hand rule indicates that the current is clockwise when viewed from above the north pole.

90   (a) The tube should be oriented so that the magnetic field inside the coil opposes Earth's magnetic field. Thus, the tube should be lined up with Earth's magnetic field. (b) 26.0 mA

91   3.18 cm

92   (a) $B=\left(\dfrac{\mu_0}{2\pi}\dfrac{I}{R}\right)\sin\theta=\dfrac{\mu_0 I}{2\pi R}\dfrac{a}{\sqrt{a^2+R^2}}$

      (b) $B_N=N\dfrac{\mu_0 I}{2\pi R}\sin\left(\dfrac{\pi}{N}\right)$ $N=3,\ 4,\ \text{K}$

$$B_\infty=\text{Limit}_{N\to\infty}\,N\dfrac{\mu_0 I}{2\pi R}\sin\left(\dfrac{\pi}{N}\right)=\dfrac{\mu_0 I}{2\pi R}\,\text{Limit}_{N\to\infty}\,N\dfrac{\pi}{N}=\dfrac{\mu_0 I}{2R}$$

93   (a) and (b) $B(5.0\,\text{cm})=B(10\,\text{cm})=10\,\mu\text{T}$ (c) $B(20\,\text{cm})=5.0\,\mu\text{T}$

94   (a) $-(2.0\,\mu\text{N}\cdot\text{m})\hat{i}$ (b) $(20\,\mu\text{N})\hat{j}$

95   2.24 A

96   44.7 mA

97   (c) $B_z=\tfrac{1}{2}\mu_0\omega\sigma\left(\dfrac{R^2+2z^2}{\sqrt{R^2+z^2}}-2z\right)$

98   (a) $\vec{B}=\dfrac{\mu_0 I\ell^2}{2\pi\left(z^2+\dfrac{\ell^2}{4}\right)\sqrt{z^2+\dfrac{\ell^2}{2}}}\hat{k}$

Chapter 28
Magnetic Induction

1   (*a*) Orient the sheet so the normal to the sheet is both horizontal and perpendicular to the local tangent to the magnetic equator. (*b*) Orient the sheet of paper so the normal to the sheet is perpendicular to the direction of the normal described in the answer to part (*a*).

2   (*a*) Orient the sheet so the normal to the sheet is vertical.

5   (*d*)

6   (*a*) Counterclockwise (*b*) Clockwise

7   The induced current is closkwise as viewed from the left. The loops repel each other.

8

    (*a*) and (*b*)

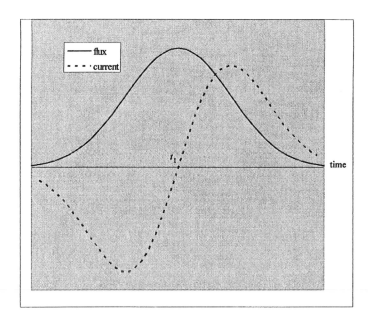

9 (*a*) and (*b*)

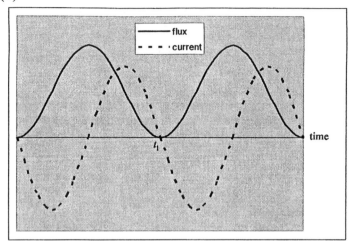

10 In the configuration shown in (*a*), energy is dissipated by eddy currents from the emf induced by the pendulum movement. In the configuration shown in (*b*), the slits inhibit the eddy currents and the braking effect is greatly reduced.

11 The magnetic field of the falling magnet sets up eddy currents in the metal tube. The eddy currents establish a magnetic field that exerts a force on the magnet opposing its motion; thus, the magnet is slowed down. If the tube is made of a nonconducting material, there are no eddy currents.

12 (*a*) There is no induced current. (*b*) counterclockwise (*c*) clockwise

13 (*c*)

14 (*a*) A (*b*) 9

15 (*a*) False (*b*) True (*c*) False (*d*) True (*e*) False

16 1 mV. There is no danger of being shocked and no reason to switch to wooden bats.

17 $u_m \approx \left(8 \times 10^3\right) u_e$

18 (*a*) 5 rev/s (*b*) 0.8 mV

19 (*a*) 0.5 V (*b*) 7 mV/m

20 (*a*) 0.50 mWb (*b*) 0.43 mWb (*c*) 0.25 mW (*d*) 0

21 (*a*) 0 (*b*) 14 μWb (*c*) 0 (*d*) 12 μWb

22   (*a*) 42 mWb (*b*) 21 mWb

23 $\phi_m = \pm \pi R^2 B$

24   758 μWb

25   6.74 mWb

26   (*a*) 30.2 mWb (*b*) 0 (*c*) 21.3 mWb (*d*) 0 (*e*) 18 mWb

27   (*a*) $\phi_m = \mu_0 n I N \pi R_1^2$ (*b*) $\phi_m = \mu_0 n I N \pi R_2^2$

28   (*a*) $\phi_m = \dfrac{\mu_0 I b}{2\pi} \ln\left(\dfrac{d+a}{d} \right)$ (*b*) 0.50 μWb

29 $\dfrac{\phi_m}{L} = \dfrac{\mu_0 I}{4\pi}$

30   (*a*) $\varepsilon(t) = -(0.20t - 0.40)\text{V}$, where ε is in volts and t is in seconds.
   (*b*)

t	ϕ_m	ε
(s)	(Wb)	(V)
0	0	0.40
2.0	−0.40	0.00
4.0	0.0	−0.40
6.0	1.2	−0.8

31 (*a*)

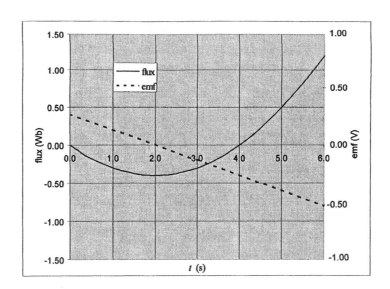

(*b*) The flux is a minimum when *t* = 2.0 s and that *V*(2.0 s) = 0.

(*c*) The flux is zero when *t* = 0 and *t* = 4.0 s. $\mathcal{E}(0) = 0.40$ V and $\mathcal{E}(4.0\ \text{s}) = -0.40$ V.

32 (*a*) 3.1 mWb (*b*) 2.2 mV

33 (*a*) 1.26 mC (*b*) 12.6 mA (*c*) 628 mV

34 (*a*) 800 μA (*b*) 280 μC

35 79.8 μT

36 (*a*) 6.4×10^{-20} N (*b*) 0.40 V/m (*c*) 0.12 V

37 400 m/s

38 (*a*) 1.6 V (*b*) 0.80 A (*c*) 0.13 N (*d*) 1.3 W (*e*) 1.3 W

39 (*a*)

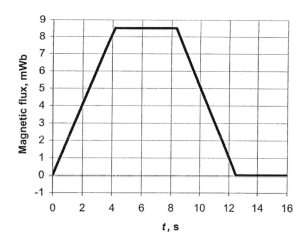

(*b*)

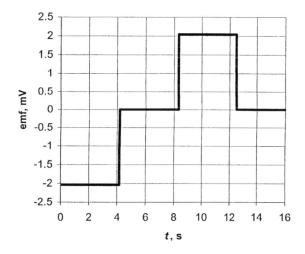

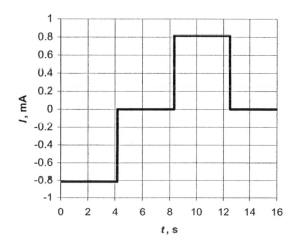

40 (a) $\mathcal{E} = -(1.4\,\text{V})\sin\left[(120\pi\ \text{rad/s})t\right]$ (b) 1.4 V

41 (a) $F_{\text{m}} = \dfrac{B\ell}{R}(\mathcal{E} - B\ell v)$ (c) 0

42 (a) 0.314 mV (b) 0.785 mA (c) 0.247 μW

45 (a) 14 V (b) 486 rev/s

46 0.71 T

47 (a) 24.0 Wb (b) −1.60 kV

48 1.89 mH

49 $L = 0$, $R = 162\ \Omega$

51 0.16 μH

52 12.0 mH

54 (a) 2.00 A (b) 4.00 J

56 (a) 54 mJ (b) 0.45 kJ/m^3

57 $\dfrac{dU_m}{dx} = \dfrac{\mu_0 I^2}{16\pi}$

58 (a) 7.96×10^3 (b) $B = 2.55\ \text{T}$, $u_{\text{m}} = 2.58\,\text{MJ/m}^3$ (c) 5.09 kJ

59 (a) $I = 0$, $dI/dt = 25.0$ kA/s (b) $I = 2.27$ A, $dI/dt = 20.5$ kA/s
(c) $I = 7.90$ A, $dI/dt = 9.20$ kA/s (d) $I = 10.8$ A, $dI/dt = 3.38$ kA/s

60 (a) 13.5 mA (b) 0

61 (a) 44.1 W (b) 40.4 W (c) 3.62 W

62 (a) 2.3 (b) 4.6 (c) 6.91

63 (a) 3.00 kA/s (b) 1.50 kA/s (c) 80.0 mA (d) 0.123 ms

64 (a) 2.4 s (b) 20 s

65 (*a*) $I_{10\text{-}\Omega} = I_{2\text{-H}} = 1.0$ A, $I_{100\text{-}\Omega} = 0$ (*b*) $V_{2\text{-H}} = 100$ V

(*c*)

Cell	Formula/Content	Algebraic Form
B1	2.0	L
B2	100	R
B3	1	I_0
A6	0	t_0
B6	$B$3*EXP((–$B$2/$B$1)*A6)	$I_0 e^{-\frac{R}{L}t}$

	A	B	C
1	$L=$	2	H
2	$R=$	100	ohms
3	$I_0=$	1	A
4			
5	t	$I(t)$	$V(t)$
6	0.000	1.00E+00	100.00
7	0.005	7.79E–01	77.88
8	0.010	6.07E–01	60.65
9	0.015	4.72E–01	47.24
10	0.020	3.68E–01	36.79
11	0.025	2.87E–01	28.65
12	0.030	2.23E–01	22.31
32	0.130	1.50E–03	0.15
33	0.135	1.17E–03	0.12
34	0.140	9.12E–04	0.09
35	0.145	7.10E–04	0.07
36	0.150	5.53E–04	0.06

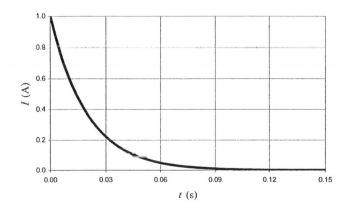

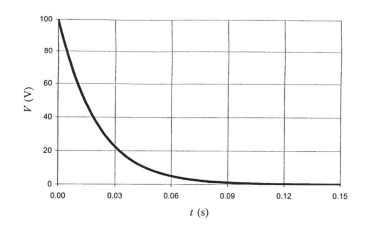

66   (a) $I_{battery} = I_{100\ ohm} = 90.9$ mA, $I_L = 0$ (b) $I_{battery} = 1.00$ A, $I_{100\ ohm} = 0$,
$I_L = 1.00$ A (c) $I_{battery} = 0$, $I_{100\ ohm} = -1.00$ A, $I_L = 1.00$ A
(d) $I_{battery} = I_{100\ ohm} = I_L = 0$

67   (a) 88 ms (b) 35 mH

68   231 μs

69   (a) 3.53 J (b) 1.61 J (c) 1.92 J

70   (a) 199 T/s (b) 212 T/s

71   (b) 2.50 krad/s

72   0.475 V. The maximum induced emf occurs at the instant the normal to the
plane of the coil is perpendicular to the magnetic field $\vec{B}$.

75   0.28 H

76   (a) 370 mA (b) 103 W. A power of 103 W is equal to 0.137 hp. Your
friend is likely to tire. This is probably not an efficient way to generate
power.

77   (a) As the magnet passes through a loop it induces an emf because of the
changing flux through the loop. This allows the coil to "sense" when the
magnet is passing through it. (b) One cannot use a cylinder made of
conductive material because eddy currents induced in it by a falling magnet
would slow the magnet. (c) As the magnet approaches the loop, the flux
increases, resulting in the negative voltage signal of increasing magnitude.
When the magnet is passing a loop, the flux reaches a maximum value and
then decreases, so the induced emf becomes zero and then positive. The

instant at which the induced emf is zero is the instant at which the magnet is at the center of the loop.

(d)

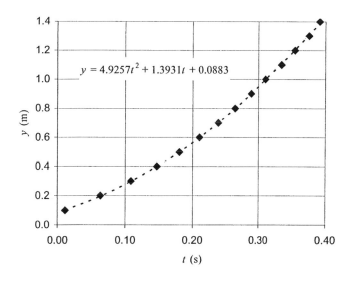

$$y = 4.9257t^2 + 1.3931t + 0.0883$$

$$g = 9.85\,\text{m/s}^2$$

78　(a) 0 (b) 0.23 A, clockwise (c) 0 (d) 0.23 A, counterclockwise

79　(a) $E_{r<R} = -\frac{1}{2}r\mu_0 nI_0\omega\cos\omega t$ (b) $E_{r>R} = -\frac{\mu_0 nR^2 I_0\omega}{2r}\cos\omega t$

80　(a) $B(r<r_1)=0$, $B(r_1<r<r_2)=\frac{\mu_0 I}{2\pi r}$, $B(r>r_2)=0$

82　(a) $I = \frac{B\ell}{R}v$, clockwise (b) $F = \frac{B^2 l^2}{R}v$. The magnetic force is upward. (c)

$F_{\text{net}} = mg - \frac{B^2\ell^2}{R}v$ (d) $mg - \frac{B^2 l^2}{R}v = m\frac{dv}{dt}$ (e) $v(t) = v_t\left(1 - e^{-t/\tau}\right)$, where

$v_t = \frac{mgR}{B^2 l^2}$ and $\tau = \frac{v_t}{g}$. (f) $y(t) = v_t\left[t - \tau\left(1 - e^{t/\tau}\right)\right]$

(g)

Cell	Formula/Content	Algebraic Form
B1	0.0500	m
B2	0.200	R
B3	0.400	B
B4	0.300	L
B5	$B$1*$B$7*$B$2/($B$3^2*$B$4^2)	v_t
B6	$B$5/$B$7	τ

B7	9.81	g
A10	0.00	t
B10	\$B\$5*(A10−\$B\$6*(1−EXP(−A10/\$B\$6)))	y
C10	0.5*\$B\$7*A10^2	$\frac{1}{2}gt^2$

	A	B	C
1	$m=$	0.0500	kg
2	$R=$	0.200	ohms
3	$B=$	0.400	T
4	$L=$	0.300	m
5	$v_t=$	6.813	m/s
6	$\tau=$	0.694	s
7	$g=$	9.81	m/s^2
8			
9	t	y	y (no B)
10	0.00	0.000	0.000
11	0.01	0.000	0.000
12	0.02	0.002	0.002
71	0.61	1.390	1.825
72	0.62	1.430	1.885

$y(0.61 \text{ s}) = 1.4$ m. In the absence of the magnetic field, $y(0.53 \text{ s}) = 1.4$ m.

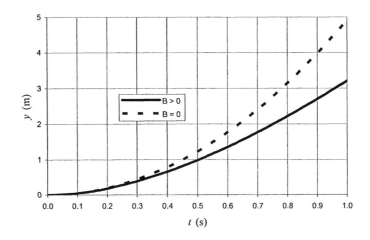

In the absence of the magnetic field, the loop falls, a distance of 1.40 m in about 0.08 s, less time than it takes to fall the same distance in the presence of the magnetic field.

Chapter 29
Alternating-Current Circuits

1   8.33 ms

2   (*a*)

3   (*b*)

4   (*a*)

5   (*c*)

6   Yes to both questions. (*a*) While the magnitude of the current in the inductor is increasing, the inductor absorbs power from the generator. (*b*) When the magnitude of the current in the inductor decreases, the inductor supplies power to the generator.

7   Yes to both questions. (*a*) While the magnitude of the charge is accumulating on either plate of the capacitor, the capacitor absorbs power from the generator. (*b*) When the magnitude of the charge is on either plate of the capacitor is decreasing, it supplies power to the generator.

9   (*a*)

10   (*b*)

11   (*a*)

12   (*a*) True (*b*) True (*c*) True (*d*) True

13   (*a*) False (*b*) False (*c*) True (*d*) True (*e*) True (*f*) True

14   Because the power curves received by your radio from two stations have width, you could have two frequencies overlapping as a result of receiving signals from both stations.

15   (*a*) True (*b*) False (*c*) True

16   (*a*)

17   (*a*) False (*b*) True (*c*) True (*d*) True (*e*) True (*f*) True

18   (*a*) $R = 0.57$ kΩ, $X_L = 0.27$ kΩ (*b*) 63 A, 40.3 kV (*c*) 21 kW (*d*) \$128
(*e*) 33 μF

19   (*a*) 0.833 A (*b*) 1.18 A (*c*) 200 W

20   (*a*) 21 A (*b*) 1.8 kW

21   (*a*) 0.38 Ω (*b*) 3.77 Ω (*c*) 37.7 Ω

22   (*a*) 0.20 H (*b*) 0.20 kΩ

23   1.6 kHz

24   (*a*) 2.65 MΩ (*b*) 26.5 kΩ (*c*) 26.5 Ω

25   (*a*) 25 mA (*b*) 18 mA

26   (*a*) 16 kHz (*b*) 0.16 kHz (*c*) 1.6 MHz

27   (*a*) 0.35 A (*b*) 0.35 A
(*c*) $I = (0.34\,\text{A})\cos(\omega t + 0.17\,\text{rad})$

29   (*a*) 1.3 ms (*b*) 88 mH

30   (*b*) The circuit with capacitance $2C_0$ has the greatest peak current.

31   (*a*) 2.3 mJ (*b*) 0.71 kHz (*c*) 0.67 A

32   (*a*) 24.0 V (*b*) 0.576 mJ (*c*) 178 Hz (*d*) 447

33   (*a*)

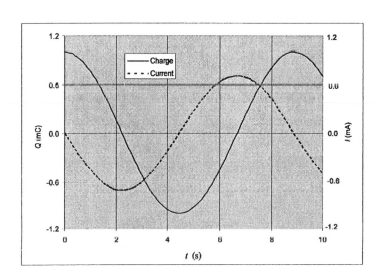

34 (*a*) 0.40 kΩ (*b*) 71 V

35 29.2 mH

36 (*a*) $V_{out} = (9.95\,\text{V})\left[\cos\omega_1 t + \cos\omega_2 t\right]$, where $\omega_1 = 100$ rad/s and $\omega_2 = 10\,000$ rad/s. (*b*) 10:1

37 (*a*) 0.33 (*b*) 27 Ω (*c*) 0.20 H (*d*) Because the circuit is inductive, the current lags the voltage. (*e*) 71°

38 (*a*) 7.9 A (*b*) $V_{L,\text{peak}} = 345\,\text{V}$, $V_{L,\text{rms}} = 244\,\text{V}$ (*c*) 1.3 kW
(*d*) $U_{L\,\text{peak}} = 1.1\,\text{J}, U_{L,\text{av}} = 0.57\,\text{J}$

39 0.397

41 (*a*) $I_{\text{rms}} = 6.23\,\text{A}, I_{R_L\,\text{rms}} = 2.80\,\text{A}, I_{L\,\text{rms}} = 5.53\,\text{A}$
(*b*) $I_{\text{rms}} = 3.28\,\text{A}, I_{R_L\,\text{rms}} = 2.94\,\text{A}, I_{L\,\text{rms}} = 1.46\,\text{A}$
(*c*) 50.2% (*d*) 80.0%

42 (*a*) $P_1 = 46\,\text{W}, P_2 = 52\,\text{W}$ (*b*) $P_1 = 46\,\text{W}, P_2 = 45\,\text{W}$
(*c*) $P_1 = 46\,\text{W}, P_2 = 34\,\text{W}$

43 60 V

45 (*a*) $\delta = \tan^{-1}\left[-1/(\omega RC)\right]$ (*b*) $\delta \to -90°$ (*c*) $\delta \to 0$ (*d*) For very low driving frequencies, $X_C \gg R$, so $\vec{V}_C$ effectively lags $\vec{V}_{in}$ by 90°. For very high driving frequencies, $X_C \ll R$, so $\vec{V}_R$ is effectively in phase with $\vec{V}_{in}$.

46 (*a*) 0.53 kHz
(*b*)

	A	B	C	D	E	F
1	$R=$	2.00E+04	ohms			
2	$C=$	1.50E−08	F			
3	$V_{\text{in peak}}=$	1	V			
4	$f_{3\,\text{dB}}=$	531	Hz			
5						
6						
7	f	log(f)	V_{out}	log(V_{out})	delta(rad)	delta(deg)
8	53	1.72	0.099	−1.003	−1.471	−84.3
9	63	1.80	0.118	−0.928	−1.453	−83.2

| 533 | 5303 | 3.72 | 0.995 | −0.002 | −0.100 | −5.7 |
| 534 | 5313 | 3.73 | 0.995 | −0.002 | −0.100 | −5.7 |

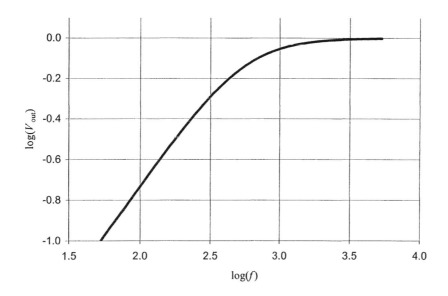

(c)

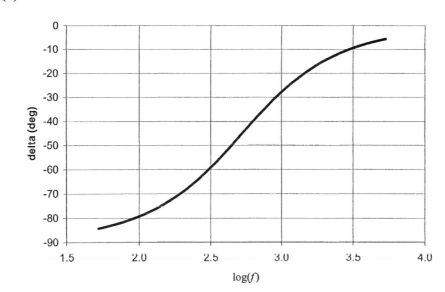

When $f = f_{3\,dB}$, $\delta \approx \boxed{-44.9°}$. This result is in good agreement with its calculated value of $-45.0°$.

50   13 nF

51 (*b*) Note that, as $\omega \to 0$, $V_L \to V_{peak}$. This makes sense physically in that, for low frequencies, X_C is large and, therefore, a larger peak voltage will appear across it than appears across it for high frequencies.

Note further that, as $\omega \to \infty$, $V_L \to 0$. This makes sense physically in that, for high frequencies, X_C is small and, therefore, a smaller peak voltage will appear across it than appears across it for low frequencies.

52 (*a*) $\delta = \tan^{-1}(\omega RC)$ (*b*) As $\omega \to 0$, $\delta \to 0°$. This behavior makes sense physically in that, at low frequencies, X_C is very large compared to R and, as a consequence, V_C is in phase with V_{in}. As $\omega \to \infty$, $\delta \to 90°$. This behavior makes sense physically in that, at high frequencies, X_C is very small compared to R and, as a consequence, V_C is out of phase with V_{in}.

53

Cell	Formula/Content	Algebraic Form
B1	2.00E+03	R
B2	5.00E−09	C
B3	1	$V_{in\ peak}$
B8	$B$3/SQRT(1+((2*PI()*A8* 1000*$B$1*$B$2)^2))	$\dfrac{V_{in\ peak}}{\sqrt{1+(2\pi fRC)^2}}$
C8	ATAN(2*PI()*A8*1000*$B$1*$B$2)	$\tan^{-1}(2\pi fRC)$
D8	C8*180/PI()	δ in degrees

	A	B	C	D
1	R=	1.00E+04	ohms	
2	C=	5.00E−09	F	
3	$V_{in\ peak}$=	1	V	
4				
5				
6	f(kHz)	V_{out}	δ(rad)	δ(deg)
7	0	1.000	0.000	0.0
8	1	0.954	0.304	17.4
56	49	0.065	1.506	86.3
57	50	0.064	1.507	86.4

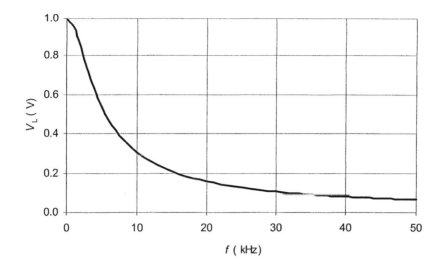

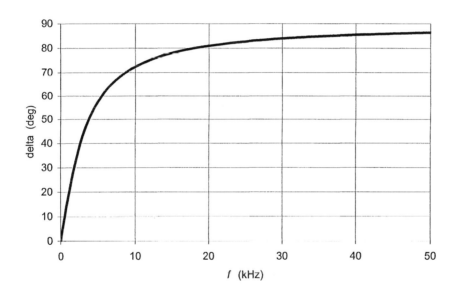

55 (*b*) $\Delta\omega = \dfrac{R}{L}$

56

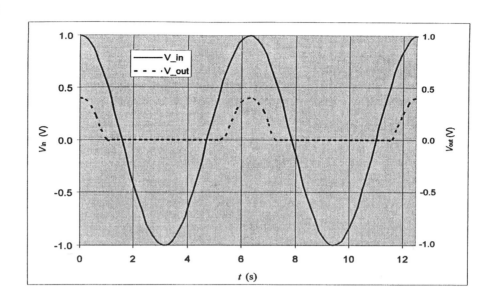

57 33 μF

58 (a) $I_{L\,\text{peak}} = \dfrac{25.0\,\text{V/H}}{2\pi f}$, lagging $\mathcal{E}$ by $90°$,

$I_{C\,\text{peak}} = (2.50\,\text{mV}\cdot\text{F}) \times 2\pi f$, leading $\mathcal{E}$ by $90°$ (b) 100 rad/s

(c) $I_L = (250\,\text{mA})\cos\left(\omega t - \dfrac{\pi}{2}\right)$, $I_C = -(250\,\text{mA})\cos\left(\omega t + \dfrac{\pi}{2}\right)$, where

$\omega = 100$ rad/s.

(d)

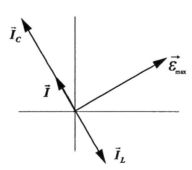

59 (a) $I(t) = -(19\,\text{mA})\sin\left(\omega t + \dfrac{\pi}{4}\right)$, where $\omega = 1250$ rad/s. (b) 23 μF

(c) $U_m(t) = (4.9\,\mu\text{J})\sin^2\left(\omega t + \dfrac{\pi}{4}\right)$, $U_e(t) = (4.9\,\mu\text{J})\cos^2\left(\omega t + \dfrac{\pi}{4}\right)$, where

$\omega = 1250$ rad/s. $U = 4.9\,\mu\text{J}$

60 1.22×10^9 N/m^2

61 (*a*) 5.4 fF (*b*) $f(x) = \dfrac{70\,\text{MHz}}{\sqrt{1 - (4.0\,\text{m}^{-1})x}}$

62 (*a*) 0.54 (*b*) 95 mA (*c*) 0.73 W

64 (*a*) 7.1×10^3 rad/s (*b*) 14 A (*c*) $X_C = 63\,\Omega$, $X_L = 80\,\Omega$ (*d*) 18 Ω (*e*) 3.9 A
(*f*) 74°

65 (*a*) 14 (*b*) 80 Hz (*c*) 0.27

66 2.0×10^3

67 (*a*) 10 A (*b*) 53° (*c*) 0.33 mF (*d*) 0.13 kV

68 (*a*) 19 μF (*b*) 25 V

69 (*a*) 80 V (*b*) 78 V (*c*) 0.17 kV (*d*) 0.11 kV (*e*) 0.18 kV

70 (*a*) 0.93 kW (*b*) 7.7 Ω (*c*) 0.10 mF (*d*) +41 μF (*e*) +20 mH

71
(*a*)

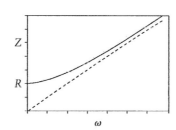

(*b*)

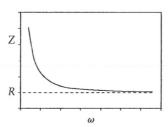

(*c*)

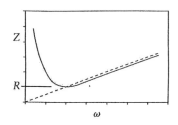

72 (*a*) 3.00 A (*b*) $8.00\,\text{mH} < L < 8.38\,\text{mH}$ and $31.6\,\text{mH} < L < 40.0\,\text{mH}$

73 (*a*) $Z = 12\ \Omega$ (*b*) $R = 7.2\ \Omega$, $X = 10\ \Omega$ (*c*) If the current leads the emf, the reactance is capacitive.

74 (*a*) 4.0 mH (*b*) 71 mA

78 (*a*) 3.55 mH (*b*) 0.198 pF (*c*) 3.7×10^{-4}

79 (*a*) 1:5 (*b*) 50 A

80 (*a*) Because there are fewer turns in the secondary than in the primary, it is a step-down transformer. (*b*) 2.40 V (*c*) 5.00 A

81 (*a*) 1.5 A (*b*) 19

82 (*a*) 15.8 (*b*) 16.0 mW

83 3.33×10^{3}

84 (*a*) 6.1 A (*b*) 0.44 kW (*c*) 73 V

85 (*a*) 12 V (*b*) 8.5 V

86 $I_{\text{av},a} = 2.0\,\text{A}$, $I_{\text{rms},a} = 2.3\,\text{A}$, $I_{\text{av},b} = 2.0\,\text{A}$, $I_{\text{rms},b} = 2.8\,\text{A}$

87 $I_{\text{max}} = 1.06\,\text{A}$, $I_{\text{min}} = -0.06\,\text{A}$, $I_{\text{av}} = 0.50\,\text{A}$, $I_{\text{rms}} = 0.64\,\text{A}$

88 $I_{\text{min}} = -45\,\text{mA}$, $I_{\text{max}} = 45\,\text{mA}$, $I_{\text{av}} = 0$, $I_{\text{rms}} = 32\,\text{mA}$

Chapter 30
Maxwell's Equations and Electromagnetic Waves

1   (*a*) False (*b*) True (*c*) True (*d*) False

3   (*a*) False (*b*) True (*c*) True (*d*) True

4    $\oint_S B_n \, dA = \mu_0 q_{m, \text{inside}}$

5   (*a*) (1) X rays (2) green light (3) red light (*b*) (1) microwaves (2) green light (3) ultraviolet light

6   (*a*) False (*b*) True (*c*) False

7   (*a*) The electric dipole antenna should be oriented vertically. (*b*) The loop antenna and the electric dipole transmitting antenna should be in the same vertical plane.

9   (*d*)

10   (*d*)

11   (*d*)

12   (*a*) 1.4×10^5 m/s^2 (*b*) 2.1 ms

13   2×10^{-7}

14   (*a*) If the sail is highly reflective rather than highly absorptive, the radiation force is doubled. (*c*) $\Gamma_r / \Gamma_g = 5.4 \times 10^{-4}$ for $A = 177$ m^2 and $m = 500$ kg. This scheme is not likely to work effectively. For any reasonable spacecraft mass, the surface mass density of the sail would have to be extremely small (experimental sails have area densities of approximately 3 g/m^2), while the sail itself would have to be huge. Additionally, unless struts are built into the sail, it would collapse during use.

15   (*a*) 3.4×10^{14} V/(m·s)

16   0.89 nA

18   (*b*) $I_d = -(23.6 \, \mu\text{A}) \sin 500\pi t$

19 (a) 10 A (b) $\dfrac{dE}{dt} = 2.3 \times 10^{12} \, \dfrac{V}{m \cdot s}$ (c) $\oint_{C} \vec{B} \cdot d\vec{\ell} = 0.79 \, \mu T \cdot m$

21 580 nm, 5.17×10^{14} Hz

22 (a) 10.0 GHz (b) 0.84

23 (a) 3.00×10^{18} Hz (b) 5.45×10^{14} Hz. Consulting Table 30-1, we see that the color of light with a wavelength of 550 nm is yellow-green. This result is consistent with those of Problem 21 and is close to the wavelength of the peak output of the Sun. Because we see naturally by reflected sunlight, this result is not surprising.

24 (a) $I(90°, 30\,m) = \frac{1}{9} I_1$ (b) $I(45°, 10\,m) = \frac{1}{2} I_1$ (c) $I(30°, 20\,m) = \frac{1}{16} I_1$

25 (a) 30° (b) 7.1 m

26 18.2 pW/m^2

27 4.13 μW/m^2

28 1.51 mW

29 386 nW/m^2

30 (a) 194 V/m (b) 0.647 μT

31 (a) 283 V/m (b) 0.943 μT (c) 212 W/m^2 (d) 0.708 μPa

32 (a) 1.33 μT (b) 1.42 μJ/m^3 (c) 425 W/m^2

33 (a) 40 nN (b) 80 nN

34 69 nN

35 (a) 45° (b) 5.7°

36 (a) 3.00 m (b) 531 kJ/m^3 (c) $E_{rms} = 245\,MV/m$, $B_{rms} = 0.817\,T$

37 (a) $+x$ direction (b) $\lambda = 0.628$ m, $f = 477$ MHz
    (c) $\vec{E}(x,t) = (194\,V/m)\cos[kx - \omega t]\hat{j}$, $\vec{B}(x,t) = (647\,nT)\cos[kx - \omega t]\hat{k}$, where $k = 10.0$ rad/m and $\omega = 3.00 \times 10^{9}$ rad/s.

$\vec{B}(x,t) = (0.647\,\mu T)\cos[kx - \omega t]\hat{k}$, where $k = 10.0$ rad/m and $\omega = 3.00 \times 10^9$ rad/s.

38 (b) radially inward (c) $\vec{S} = -\dfrac{\epsilon_0}{2}\dfrac{E}{}\dfrac{dE}{dt}R\hat{R}$ $(R \leq b)$, where E is the electric field strength between the plates, R is the radial distance from the line joining the centers of the plates, and b is the radius of the plates.

39 6.10×10^{-3} degrees

40 (a) 1.5×10^5 W (b) 1.0 mN

41 (a) $F_{r\,Earth} = 5.83 \times 10^8$ N ,. $F_{r\,Earth} = (1.65 \times 10^{-14})F_{g,\,Earth}$

(b) $F_{r\,Mars} = 7.18 \times 10^7$ N , $F_{r\,Mars} = (4.27 \times 10^{-14})F_{g\,Mars}$ (c) Mars

46 (a) 3.00 m, $+z$ direction

(b) $\vec{E}(z,t) = -(3.00\,V/m)\cos[(2.09\,m^{-1})z - (6.28 \times 10^8\,s^{-1})t]\hat{j}$

(c) $\vec{S}(z,t) = (23.9\,mW/m^2)\cos^2[(2.09\,m^{-1})z - (6.28 \times 10^8\,s^{-1})t]\hat{k}$, 11.9 mW/m^2

47 2.6 mV

48 (a) 50.0 μV (b) 41.9 nV. The loop antenna should be oriented so the transmitting antenna lies in the plane of the loop.

49 (a) $I = V_0\left(\dfrac{1}{R}\sin\omega t + \dfrac{\epsilon_0\,\pi a^2}{d}\cos\omega t\right)$

(b) $B(r) = \dfrac{\mu_0 V_0}{2\pi r}\left(\dfrac{1}{R}\sin\omega t + \omega\dfrac{\epsilon_0\,\pi r^2}{d}\cos\omega t\right)$

(c) $\delta = \tan^{-1}\left(\dfrac{R\omega\,c_0\,\pi a^2}{d}\right)$

50 0.10 mN

51 (*a*)

$$\vec{S}(x,t) = \frac{1}{\mu_0 c} \left[E_{10}^2 \cos^2(k_1 x - \omega_1 t) + 2 E_{10} E_{20} \cos(k_1 x - \omega_1 t) \cos(k_2 x - \omega_2 t + \delta) + E_{20}^2 \cos^2(k_2 x - \omega_2 t + \delta) \right] \hat{i}$$

(*b*) $\vec{S}_{av} = \dfrac{1}{2\mu_0 c} \left[E_{10}^2 + E_{20}^2 \right] \hat{i}$

(*c*) $\vec{S}(x,t) = \dfrac{1}{\mu_0 c} \left[E_{10}^2 \cos^2(k_1 x - \omega_1 t) - E_{20}^2 \cos^2(k_2 x + \omega_2 t + \delta) \right] \hat{i}$

$\vec{S}_{av} = \dfrac{1}{2\mu_0 c} \left[E_{10}^2 - E_{20}^2 \right] \hat{i}$

53 (*a*) 9.16×10^{-15} T (*b*) 101 mV (*c*) 5.49 μV

54 (*a*) $E_{rms} = 718$ V/m, $B_{rms} = 2.40$ μT (*b*) 3.87×10^{26} W
(*c*) 6.36×10^7 W/m^2, 0.212 Pa

55 (*a*) $\vec{E} = \dfrac{I\rho}{\pi a^2} \hat{i}$, where $\hat{i}$ is a unit vector in the direction of the current. (*b*)

$\vec{B} = \dfrac{\mu_0 I}{2\pi a} \hat{\theta}$, where $\hat{\theta}$ is a unit vector perpendicular to $\hat{i}$ and tangent to the

surface of the conducting cylinder. (*c*) $\vec{S} = -\dfrac{I^2 \rho}{2\pi^2 a^3} \hat{r}$, where $\hat{r}$ is a unit

vector directed radially outward—away from the axis of the conducting
cylinder. (*d*) $\oiint S_n dA = I^2 R$

56 (*a*) $\vec{E} = -\frac{1}{2} n \mu_0 a r \hat{\theta}$, where $\hat{\theta}$ is a unit vector that is tangent to the circles
that are concentric with the axis of the solenoid. (*b*) $\vec{S} = -\frac{1}{2} n^2 \mu_0 a^2 R t \hat{r}$,
where $\hat{r}$ is a unit vector that points radially outward—away from the axis of
the solenoid.

(*c*) $\dfrac{dU_B}{dt} = n^2 \pi \mu_0 R^2 L a^2 t = \oint S_n dA$

57 (*a*) 0.574 μm (*b*) The critical radius is an upper limit, so particles smaller
than that radius will be blown out.

58 (*a*) At a perfectly conducting surface $\vec{E} = 0$. Therefore, the sum of the
electric fields of the incident and reflected wave must add to zero,
so $\vec{E}_i = -\vec{E}_r$. (*c*) Because $\vec{E} \times \vec{B} = \mu_0 \vec{S}$ and $\vec{S}$ is in the direction of

propagation of the wave, we see that, for the incident wave, $B_i = B_z \cos(\omega t - kx)$. Since both $\vec{S}$ and E_y are reversed for the reflected wave, $B_r = B_z \cos(\omega t + kx)$. So the magnetic field vectors are in the direction at the reflecting surface and add at that surface. Hence, $\vec{B} = 2\vec{B}_r$.

59   3.34 mN

Chapter 31
Properties of Light

1   (*c*)

2   (*a*)

3   (*b*)

4   (*a*), (*c*), and (*d*)

5   The change in atmospheric density results in refraction of the light from the Sun, bending it toward Earth (see the following figure). Consequently, the Sun can be seen even after it is just below the horizon.

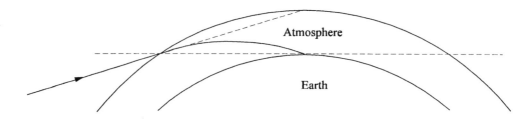

6   (*a*) Yes. (*b*) Her procedure is based on Fermat's principle of least time. The ball presumably bounces off the cushion with an angle of reflection equal to the angle of incidence, just as a light ray would do if the cushion were a mirror. The least time would also be the shortest distance of travel for the light ray.

7   The path of least time is the path through point D.

8   (*b*)

9   In resonance absorption, the molecules respond to the frequency of the light through the Einstein photon relation $E = hf$. Neither the wavelength nor the frequency of the light within the eyeball depend on the index of refraction of the medium outside the eyeball. Thus, the color appears to be the same in spite of the fact that the wavelength has changed.

10   (*b*)

11

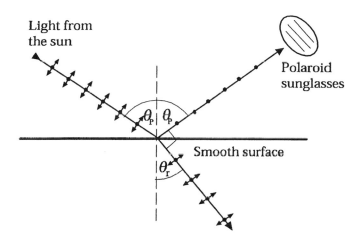

12 Molecules require that a certain minimum energy be absorbed before they ionize. The red light photons contain considerably less energy than the gamma photons, so even though there are likely to be fewer photons in the gamma beam, each one is potentially dangerous.

13 (*c*)

14 (*d*)

15 The population inversion between the state $E_{2\,Ne}$ and the state 1.96 eV below it (see Figure 31-51) is achieved by inelastic collisions between neon atoms and helium atoms excited to the state $E_{2\,He}$.

16 Although the excited atoms emit light of the same frequency on returning to the ground state, the light is emitted in a random direction, not exclusively in the direction of the incident beam. Consequently, the beam intensity is greatly diminished at this frequency.

17 (*d*)

18 $\Delta t = 2 \times 10^{-5}$ s, $\Delta t_{reaction} \approx \left(2 \times 10^{4}\right)\Delta t$. Because human reaction time is so much longer than the travel time for the light, there was no way that Galileo's experiment could demonstrate that the speed of light was not infinite.

19 3 ps

20 about 3×10^{14} photons, about 0.1 mJ

21   (*a*) 2:00 A.M., September 1 (*b*) 2:08 A.M., September 1

22   14°

23   (*a*)

24   (*a*) ±15.0 cm (*b*) 10^{-8} %

25   14 ms

26   2.0 %

28

(*a*)

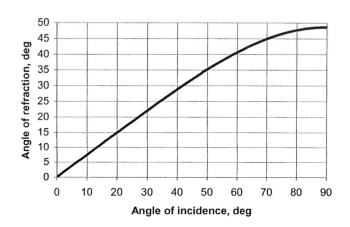

(*b*)

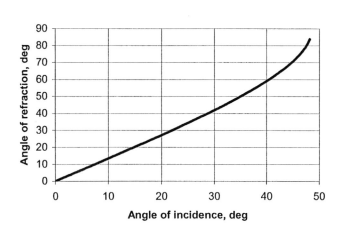

29

	(a) speed (m/s)	(b) wavelength (nm)	(c) frequency (Hz)
Air	3.00×10^8	633	4.74×10^{14}
Water	2.25×10^8	476	4.74×10^{14}
glass	2.00×10^8	422	4.74×10^{14}

30 (a) Because the index of refraction for violet light is larger than that of red light, for a given incident angle, violet light would refract more than red light. Thus, to exhibit the same refraction angle, violet light would require an angle of incidence larger than that of red light. (b) 2.49°

31 (a) 50° (b) 39° (c) 26°

32 (a) 78° (b) 53° (c) 34°

33 (a) 92% (b) 99%

34

(a)

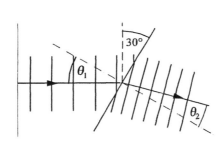

(b) 14°. As the line enters the muddy field, its speed is reduced by half and the direction of the forward motion of the line is changed. In this case, the forward motion in the muddy field makes an angle θ_2 with respect to the normal to the boundary line. Note that the separation between successive lines in the muddy field is half that in the dry field.

36 66.9° below the horizontal

37 5.1 m wide, 2.2 m deep

38 (a) $\theta_i = \sin^{-1}\left(n\sqrt{1 - \sqrt{1 - \frac{1}{n^2}}} \right)$ (b) 48.5° (c) 2.8 cm

39 48.8°

40 62.5°

41 $1.0 \times 10^2 \, \text{m}^2$

42 $2.1 \times 10^8 \, \text{m/s}$

43 1.30

45 5°

46 150 ns

47 (*a*) 62.5° (*b*) Yes, if $\theta \geq 41.8°$, where θ is the angle of incidence for the rays in glass that are incident on the glass-water boundary, the rays will leave the glass through the water and pass into the air.

48 2.2 cm

49 1.0°

50 3 μs

51 (*a*) 53.1° (*b*) 56.3°

52 67°

53 (*a*) $\frac{1}{8} I_0$ (*b*) $\frac{3}{32} I_0$

54 4.0 mW

55 (*a*) 30° (*b*) 1.7

56 (*a*) $I_3 = \frac{1}{8} I_0 \sin^2 2\theta$

57 $I_3 = \frac{1}{8} I_0 \sin^2 2\omega t$

58 (*b*)

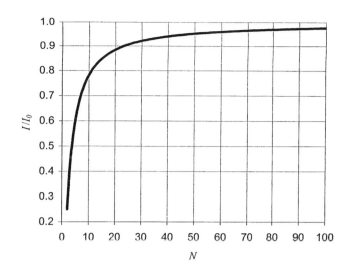

(*c*) The transmitted light, if any, is polarized parallel to the transmission axis of the last sheet. (For $N = 2$, there is no transmitted light.)

59

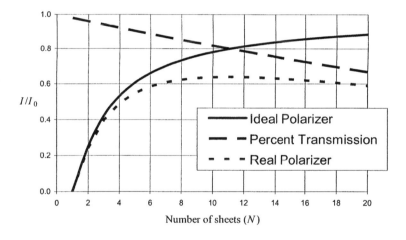

The optimum number of sheets is 11.

61 (*a*) $I_4 = 0.211I_0$ (*b*) For the single sheet between the two end sheets at $\theta = 45°$, $I_3 = 0.125I_0$. The intensity with four sheets at angles of 0°, 30°, 60° and 90° is greater the intensity of three sheets at angles of 0°, 45° and 90° by a factor of 1.69.

63 (*a*) right circularly polarized (*b*) $\vec{E} = E_0 \sin(kx + \omega t)\hat{j} - E_0 \cos(kx + \omega t)\hat{k}$

64 1.27×10^{16} photons/s

65 (*a*) 435 nm (*b*) 1210 nm

66 3.37 eV

67 (*a*) $\lambda_{max} = 388\,nm$, $\lambda_{2 \to 1} = 1140\,nm$, $\lambda_{1 \to 0} = 588\,nm$
(*b*) $\lambda_{1 \to 0} = 588\,nm$, $\lambda_{3 \to 1} = 554\,nm$

68 The energy difference between the ground state and the first excited state is $3E_0 = 40.8$ eV, corresponding to a wavelength of 30.4 nm. This is in the far ultraviolet, well outside the visible range of wavelengths. There will be no dark lines in the transmitted radiation.

69 (*a*) 15 mJ (*b*) 5.2×10^{16}

70 (*a*) 526 nm (*b*) A swimmer observes the same color in air and in water.

71 37°

73 (*a*) 36.8° (*b*) 38.7°

75 (*a*) $x = -1.00$ m (*b*) 26.6° (*c*) 26.6°

77 $\theta_{p\ silicate\ flint} = 58.3°$, $\theta_{p\ borate\ flint} = 57.5°$, $\theta_{p\ quartz} = 57.0°$, $\theta_{p\ silicate\ crown} = 56.5°$

79 (*b*) $\theta_p > \theta_c$

80 (*a*) 1.6 (*b*) 39°

81 (*a*) 1.33 (*b*) 37.2° (*c*) 48.6°. Because 48.6° is also the angle of incidence at the liquid-air interface and because it is equal to the critical angle for total internal reflection at this interface, no light will emerge into the air.

82 (*b*) $\dfrac{I_t}{I_0} = \left[\dfrac{4n}{(n+1)^2}\right]^{2N}$ (*c*) 28

83 (*c*) 1.67°

Chapter 32
Optical Images

1   Yes. Note that a virtual image is "seen" because the eye focuses the diverging rays to form a real image on the retina. For example, you can photograph the virtual image of yourself in a flat mirror and get a perfectly good picture.

2   Yes; the coordinate system and its mirror image will have opposite handedness. That is, if the coordinate system is a right-handed coordinate system, then the mirror image will be a left-handed coordinate system, and vice versa.

3   (a) False (b) False (c) True (d) False

4   (a) If $s < \frac{1}{2}R$, the image is virtual, upright, and larger than the object.
    (b) If $s < \frac{1}{2}R$, the image is virtual, upright, and larger than the object.
    (c) If $s > R$, the image is real, inverted, and smaller than the object.
    (d) If $\frac{1}{2}R < s < R$, the image is real, inverted, and larger than the object.

5   (a) The mirror will produce an upright image for all object distances.
    (b) The mirror will produce a virtual image for all object distances.
    (c) The mirror will produce an image that is that is smaller than the object for all object distances.
    (d) The mirror will never produce an enlarged image.

6   They appear more distant because in a convex mirror the angular sizes of the images are smaller than they would be in a flat mirror.

7   (b)

8 Because the index of refraction of water is greater than that of air, the rays are bent toward the normal. The diver will, therefore, think that the rays are diverging from a point above the bird, so the bird will appear to be farther from the surface than it actually is.

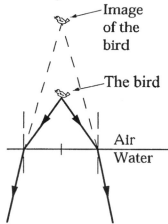

9 (*d*)

10 (*c*)

11 (*a*)

12 (*a*) True (*b*) True (*c*) False (*d*) True (*e*) False

13 The muscles in the eye change the thickness of the lens and thereby change the focal length of the lens to accommodate objects at different distances. A camera lens, on the other hand, has a fixed focal length, so that focusing is accomplished by varying the distance between the lens and the light-sensitive surface.

14 (*a*)

15 The objective lens of a microscope ordinarily produces an image that is larger than the object being viewed (see Figure 32-52), and that image is angularly magnified by the eyepiece. The objective lens of a telescope, on the other hand, ordinarily produces an image that is smaller than the object being viewed (see Figure 32-53), and that image is angularly magnified by the eyepiece. The telescope never produces a real image that is larger than the object.

16 About 1.1 cm behind the spoon, and about 2 cm.

17 $\frac{1}{2}R_{\text{Earth}}$

18 13

19

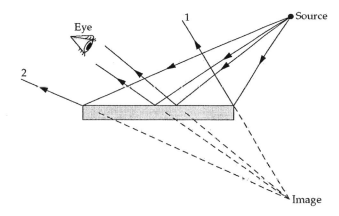

20   (*a*) 81 cm (*b*) 74 cm

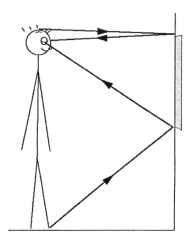

21

(a)

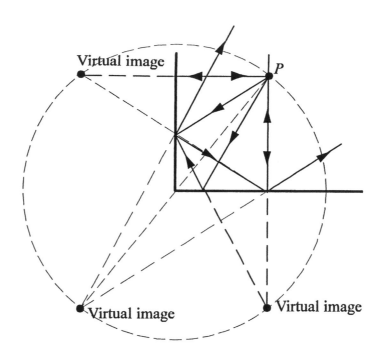

(b)

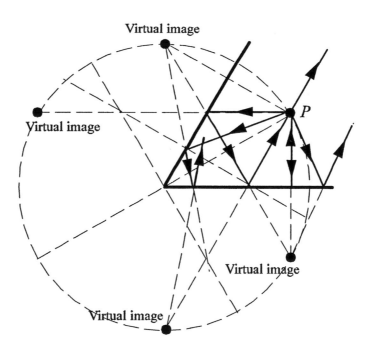

The construction details for the two virtual images behind the mirror that is at an angle of 60° with the horizontal mirror have been omitted due to the confusing detail their inclusion would add to the diagram.

(*c*)

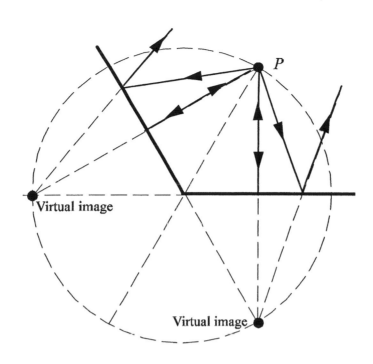

23 (*a*) For the mirror on the left, the images are located 10 cm, 50 cm, 70 cm, and 110 cm behind the mirror on the left.

(*b*) For the mirror on the right, the images are located 20 cm, 40 cm, 80 cm, and 100 cm behind the mirror on the right.

(*c*) The successive images are dimmer because the light travels farther to form them. The intensity falls off inversely with the distance the light travels. In addition, at each reflection a small percentage of the light intensity is lost. Real mirrors are not 100% reflecting.

24

(*a*) The image is real, inverted, and reduced.

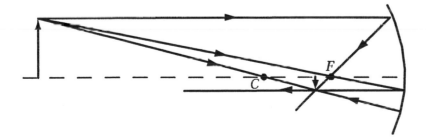

(*b*) The image is real, inverted, and the same size as the object.

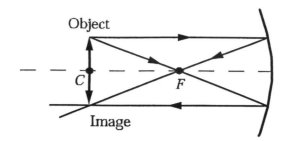

Object

Image

(c) The object is at the focal plane of the mirror. The emerging rays are parallel and do not form an image.

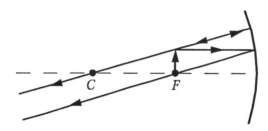

(d) The image is virtual, erect, and enlarged.

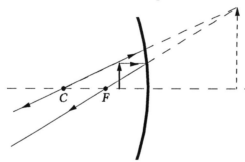

25 (a) 15 cm, 24 cm, undefined, −0.2 m (b) −0.28, −1.0, undefined, 3.0

26 (a) The image is virtual, upright, and reduced.

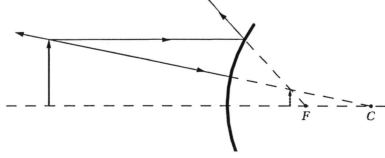

(*b*) The image is virtual, upright, and reduced.

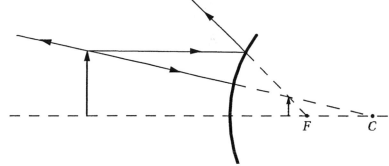

(*c*) The image is virtual, upright and reduced.

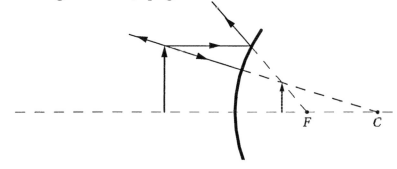

(*d*) The image is virtual, upright, and reduced.

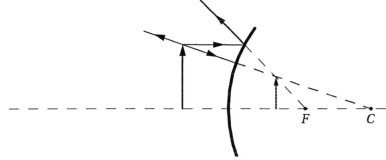

(*e*) The image is virtual, upright, and reduced.

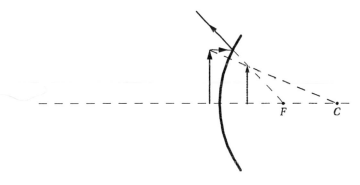

27 (*a*) −9.9 cm, − 8.0 cm, − 6.0 cm, − 4.8 cm (*b*) 0.18, 0.33, 0.50, 0.60

29 (*a*) concave (*b*) 5.1 cm

30   (*a*) 57 cm from the mirror (*b*) behind the mirror (*c*) 11 cm

31   The 3.7-cm-diameter image is 4.0 m in front of the mirror

32   (*a*) 91 cm (*b*) The mirror was moved away from the object.

33   (*a*) −1.3 m (*b*) convex

34

(*a*) $s' = 27$ cm, real

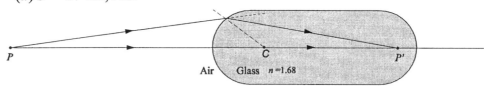

(*b*) $s' = -16$ cm, virtual

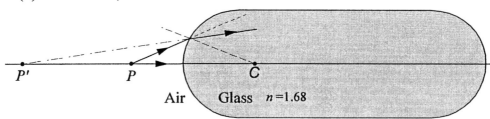

35   (*a*) $s' = 8.6$ cm (*b*) 27 cm

36 $s' = -10$ cm, virtual

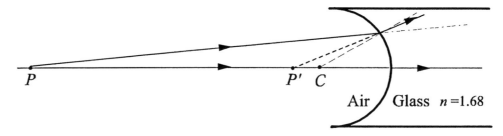

37   (*a*) $s' = -9.7$ cm, virtual

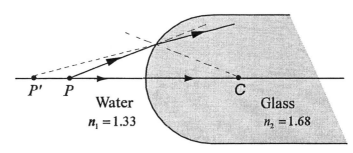

(b) $s' = -27\,\text{cm}$, virtual

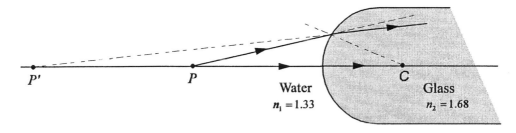

38   (a) $s' = -15\,\text{cm}$, virtual

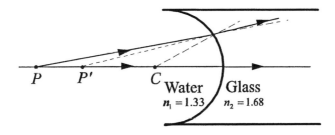

39   (a) 64 cm (b) −80 cm (c) The final image is inside the rod and 0.2 m from the surface whose radius of curvature is 8.00 cm and is virtual.

40   (a) −1.3 m (b) 15 cm (c) The final image is outside the rod and 15 cm from the end whose radius of curvature is 16.0 cm and is real.

41   (a) −30 cm (b) 22 cm from the lens and on the same side of the lens as the object (c) 0.27 (d) virtual and upright

42   (*a*) −33 cm

(*b*) 33 cm

(*c*) −33 cm

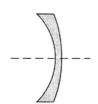

43   (*a*) 19 cm

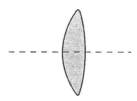

(*b*) 30 cm

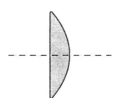

(*c*) −15 cm

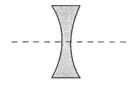

(*d*) −52 cm

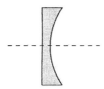

44   1.1 m

45   (*a*) $s' = 16.7\,\text{cm}$, $y' = -2.00\,\text{cm}$. Because $s' > 0$, the image is real and because $y'/y = -0.67$ cm, the image is inverted and diminished. These results confirm those obtained graphically. However, this ray diagram is not to scale.

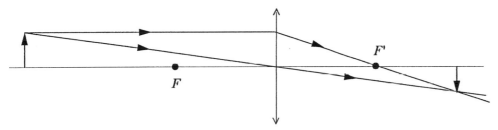

(*b*) $s' = 20.0\,\text{cm}$, $y' = -3.00\,\text{cm}$. Because $s' > 0$, the image is real. Because $y' = -3.00$ cm, the image is inverted, and the same size as the object. These results confirm those obtained from the ray diagram.

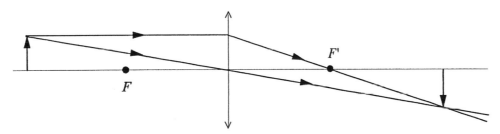

(*c*) $s' = -6.67\,\text{cm}$, $y' = 1.00\,\text{cm}$. Because $s' < 0$, the image is virtual. Because $y' = 1.00$ cm, the image is erect and about one-third the size of the object. These results are consistent with those obtained graphically.

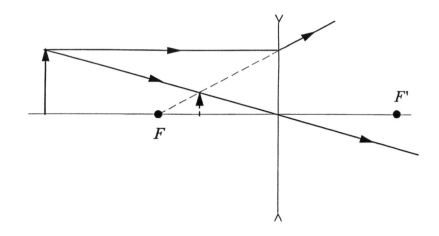

46 $r_1 = 16.2\,\text{cm}$, $r_2 = \infty$

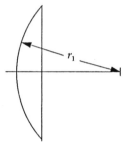

$r_1 = 32.4\,\text{cm}$, $r_2 = -32.4\,\text{cm}$

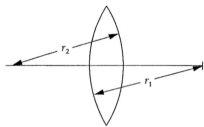

$r_1 = -6.89\,\text{cm}$, $r_2 = -12.0\,\text{cm}$

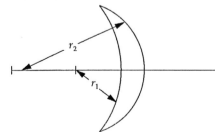

47 $r_1 = -16.2\,\text{cm}$, $r_2 = \infty$

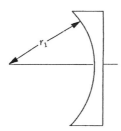

$r_1 = -32.4\,\text{cm}$, $r_2 = 32.4\,\text{cm}$

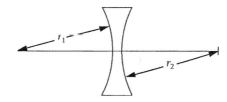

$r_1 = -5.40\,\text{cm}$, $r_2 = -8.10\,\text{cm}$

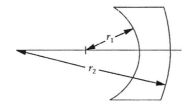

48 (a) A negative object distance means that the object is virtual; i.e., that extensions of light rays, and not the light rays themselves, converge on the object rather than diverge from it. A virtual object can occur in a two-lens system when converging rays from the first lens are incident on the second lens before they converge to form an image.

(b) $s' = 10\,\text{cm}$, $m = 0.50$. Because $s' > 0$, the image is real, and because $m > 0$, the image is erect. In addition, it is one-half the size of the virtual object.

(c) $s' = 15\,\text{cm}$, $m = 1.5$. Because $s' > 0$, the image is real, and because $m > 0$, the image is erect. In addition, it is one and one-half times the size of the virtual object.

49 (a) The final image is 85 cm to the right of the object.

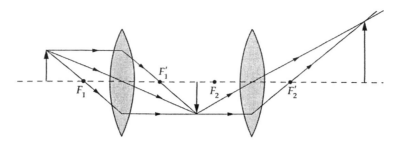

(*b*) Because $s'_2 > 0$, the image is real and because $m = m_1 m_2 = 2.0$, the image is erect and twice the size of the object.

(*c*) 2.0

50   (*a*) The final image is 48 cm to the right of the object.

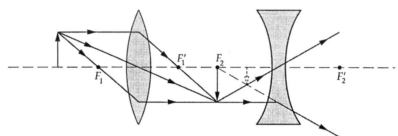

(*b*) Because $s'_2 < 0$, the image is virtual, and because $m = m_1 m_2 = -0.50$, the image is inverted and half the height of the object.

(*c*) –0.50

51   (*b*) 3.70 m

52   (*a*) and (*b*)

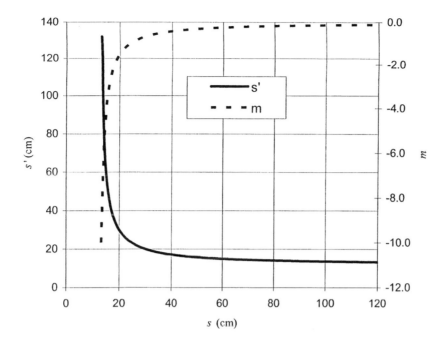

(*c*) The images are real and inverted for this range of object distances.

(*d*) The equations for the horizontal and vertical asymptotes of the graph of *s'* versus *s* are *s'* = *f* and *s* = *f*, respectively. These indicate that, as the object moves away from the lens image distance, the image moves toward the first focal point, and that, as the object moves toward the second focal point, the image distance becomes large without limit. The equations for the horizontal and vertical asymptotes of the graph of *m* versus *s* are *m* = 0 and *s* = *f*, respectively. These indicate that, as the object moves away from the lens, the image size of the image approaches zero, and that, as the object moves toward the second focal point, the image becomes large without limit.

53 (*a*) and (*b*)

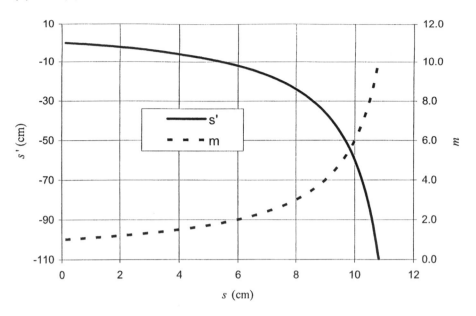

(*c*) The images are virtual and erect for this range of object distances.

(*d*) The equation for the vertical asymptote of the graph of *s'* versus *s* is *s* = *f*. This indicates that, as the object moves toward the second focal point, the magnitude of the image distance becomes large without limit. The equation for the vertical asymptote of the graph of *m* versus *s* is *s* = *f*. This indicates that, as the object moves toward the second focal point, the image becomes the large without limit. In addition, as *s* approaches zero, *s'* approaches negative infinity and *m* approaches 1, so as the object moves toward the lens, the image becomes the same size as the object and the magnitude of the image distance increases without limit.

54 (*a*) $s_2' = f_2 = 15.0 \, \text{cm}$, $m = m_2 = -1.00$. The final image is 50 cm from the object, real, inverted, and the same size as the object.

(*b*)

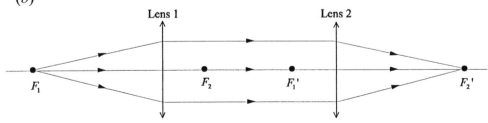

55 (*a*) $s_2' = f_2 - 15.0 \, \text{cm}$, $m = m_2 = 1.00$. The final image is 20 cm from the object, virtual, erect, and the same size as the object.

(*b*)

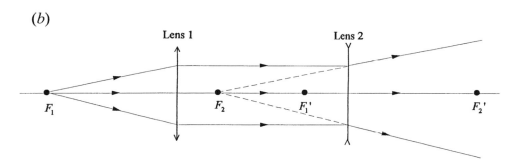

56

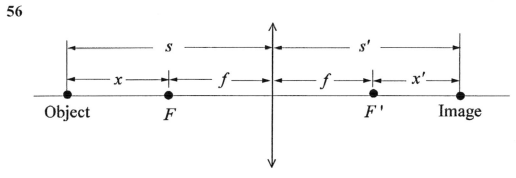

58 (*a*)

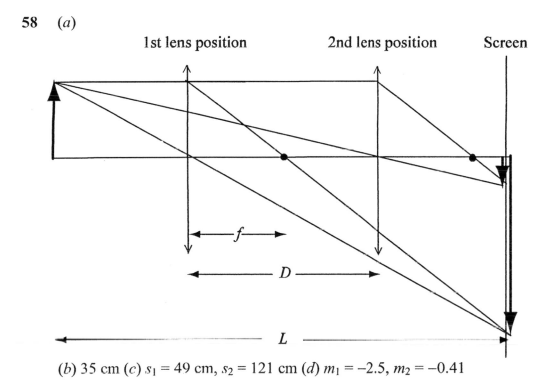

(*b*) 35 cm (*c*) $s_1 = 49$ cm, $s_2 = 121$ cm (*d*) $m_1 = -2.5$, $m_2 = -0.41$

59   (*a*) The final image is 18.7 cm to the right of the second lens. (*b*) −1.53
(*c*) Because $m < 0$, the image is inverted. Because $s_2' > 0$, the image is real.

60   (*a*)

61   Reasons for the preference for reflectors include: (1) no chromatic
aberrations, (2) less expensive to shape one side of a piece of glass than to
shape both sides, (3) reflectors can be more easily supported from rear
instead of edges, preventing sagging and focal length changes, and (4)
support from rear makes larger sizes easier to handle.

62   (*a*) 10.6 cm (*b*)   9.43 cm

63   −1.7 mm

64   44.4 cm

65   (*a*) 80.0 μrad (*b*) 1.60 mm

66   The lens would have to move 0.28 cm toward the object.

67   (*c*) $P_{min} = 40.0\,\text{D}$, $A = 4.00\,\text{D}$

68   (*b*) −2.00 D

69   (*c*) 6.0 D

70   (*a*) 1.0 m (*b*) 0.97 D

71   0.444 D

72   (*a*) 0.688 cm (*b*) The calculated value for the distance to the retina is too
large. The eye is not a homogeneous sphere, and in a real eye additional
refraction occurs at the lens. By modeling the eye as a homogeneous solid
sphere, we are ignoring the refraction that takes place at the lens.

73   3.1 D

74   (*a*) 46 cm (*b*) 1.9 m (*c*) 4.9 D

75   5.0

76 (*a*) If $x_{np} = 25$ cm, then $M = 4.2$, and if $x_{np} = 40$ cm, then $M = 6.7$. (*b*) For a person with $x_{np} = 40$ cm, the image on the retina is 1.6 times larger than it is for a person with $x_{np} = 25$ cm.

77 (*a*) 3.0 (*b*) 4.0

78 (*a*) 18.8 mm (*b*) −46.1

79 (*a*) −19 (*b*) −1.9 × 10^2

80 (*a*) 20 cm (*b*) − 4.0 (*c*) −20 (*d*) 6.3 cm

81 −230

82 (*a*) 1.67 cm (*b*) 0.508 cm (*c*) 0.496 cm

83 (*a*) 9.00 mm (*b*) 0.180 mrad and (*c*) $M = -20.0$

84 17.6 cm

85 (*a*) 25.0 (*b*) −134

86 $f_o = 28$ cm, $f_e = 4$ cm

87

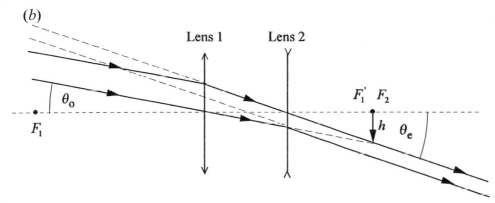

88 (*a*) 103 cm (*b*) −6.3 cm (*c*) 97 cm (*d*) 21 cm, 26

89 −6.67×10^{-3}

90 0.16 mm

91   (*a*) $s = 5.0$ cm, $s' = -10$ cm

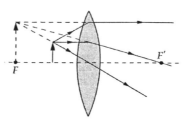

(*b*) $s = 15$ cm, $s' = 30$ cm

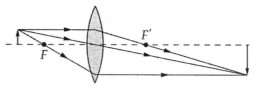

92

(*a*) The lens with a focal length of 75 mm should be the objective. The two lenses should be separated by 100 mm. The angular magnification is –3.
(*b*)

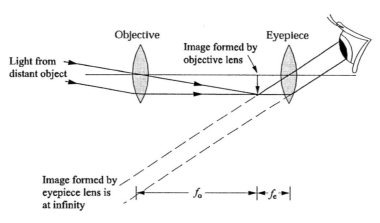

93

(*a*) The lens with a focal length of 25 mm should be the objective. The two lenses should be separated by 210 mm. The angular magnification is –21.

(*b*)

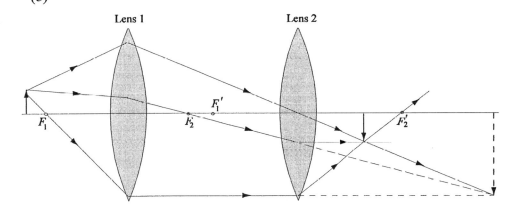

94 (*a*) 84 cm (*b*) 0.45

95 3.7 m

96 53 cm

97 (*a*) The image is 9.5 cm to the right of the second lens. (*b*) The image is about 20% larger than the object and it is inverted.

(*c*)

98 (*b*) $f_{air} = -32\,cm$, $f_{water} = -1.3\,m$

99 9.72 cm/s

100 4.24 cm

101 (*a*) The image is 18 cm from the lens, on the same side as the original object. (*b*) real and upright (*c*) To see this image, the eye must be to the left of the final image.

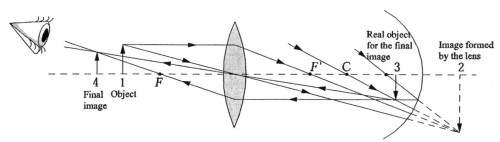

102 1.6

103 37 cm

104 1.4

105 (*a*) The final image is 3.2 cm to the left of the center of the ball. (*b*) Because s_1' is undefined, no image is formed when the object is 20.0 cm to the left of the glass ball. (Alternatively, an image is formed an infinite distance to the left of the ball.)

106 (*b*) $f \approx 17$ cm for blue light

Chapter 33
Interference and Diffraction

1   (*a*)

2   (*b*), (*c*), and (*e*)

3   The thickness of the air space between the flat glass and the lens is approximately proportional to the square of *d*, the diameter of the ring. Consequently, the separation between adjacent rings is proportional to $1/d$.

4   There are two possible reasons that fringes might not be observed. (1) The distance between adjacent fringes is so small that the fringes are not resolved by the eye. (2) Twice the thickness of the air space is greater than the coherence length of the light. If this is the case, fringes would be observed in the region close to the point where the thickness of the air space approaches zero.

5   Colors are observed when the light reflected off the front and back surfaces of the film interfere destructively for some wavelengths and constructively for other wavelengths. For this interference to occur, the phase difference between the light reflected off the front and back surfaces of the film must be constant. This means that twice the thickness of the film must be less than the coherence length of the light. The film is called a thin film if twice its thickness is less than the coherence length of the light as it traverses the film.

6   (*a*)   The phase change due to reflection from the front surface of the film is 180°; the phase change due to reflection from the back surface of the film is 0°. As the film thins toward the top, the phase change due to the path length difference between the two reflected waves (the phase difference associated with the film's thickness) becomes negligible and the two reflected waves interfere destructively.

    (*b*) The first constructive interference will arise when twice the thickness of the film is equal to half the wavelength of the color with the shortest wavelength. Therefore, the first band will be violet (shortest visible wavelength).

7   (*d*)

8   (*b*)

Chapter 33

9   (*a*)

10   (*a*)

11   (*a*)

12   Equation 33-2 expresses the condition for an intensity maximum in two-slit interference. Here *d* is the slit separation, λ the wavelength of the light, *m* an integer, and θ_m the angle at which the interference maximum appears. Equation 33-11 expresses the condition for an intensity minimum in single-slit diffraction. Here, *a* is the width of the slit, λ the wavelength of the light, θ_m the angle at which the minimum appears, and *m* is a nonzero integer.

13   (*a*)

14   (*c*)

15   (*a*) False (*b*) True (*c*) True (*d*) True (*e*) True

16   (*d*)

17   The condition for the resolution of the two sources is given by Rayleigh's criterion: $\alpha_c = 1.22\dfrac{\lambda}{D}$ (Equation 33-25), where α_c is the critical angular separation, *D* is the diameter of the aperture, and λ is the wavelength of the light illuminating (or emitted by) the objects, in this case headlights, to be resolved. Because the diameter of the pupils of your eyes are larger at night, the critical angle is smaller at night, which means that at night you can resolve the light as coming from two distinct sources when they are at a greater distance.

18   This claim is probably false. Because the minimum width that is resolvable from low-Earth orbit (250 km) is 24 m and the width of the Great Wall is 5 to 8 m high and 5 m wide, this claim is likely false. However, it is easily seen using binoculars, and pictures can be taken of it using a camera. This is because both binoculars and cameras have apertures that are larger than the pupil of the human eye. (The Chinese astronaut Yang Liwei reported that he was not able to see the wall with the naked eye during the first Chinese manned space flight in 2003.)

19   (*a*) 11 km (*b*) 9.6 km

20   Between 0.80 and 0.90 kHz

21 $5.9\,c \cdot y$

22 (*a*) 376 nm (*b*) 5.32 (*c*) 1.1 rad

23 ≈ 2.9 rad

24 (*a*) The first band is dark because the phase difference due to reflection by the bottom surface of the top plate and the top surface of the bottom plate is 180°.
(*b*) 1.75×10^{-4} rad

25 5.5 μm $< d <$ 5.8 μm

26 167

27 (*a*) 600 nm (*b*) 720 nm, 514 nm, and 400 nm (*c*) 720 nm, 514 nm, and 400 nm

28 533 nm

29 476 nm

30 603 nm

31 (*c*) 68 (*d*) 1.14 cm (*e*) The fringes would become more closely spaced.

32 0.721 mm, 1.25 mm

33 0.535 mm, 0.926 mm

34 8.33 cm^{-1}

35 4.95 mm

36 (*a*) 9.3 μm (*b*) 29

37 (*a*) 50.0 μm (*b*) According to the Raleigh criterion, you could resolve them, but not by much. (*c*) 0.500 mm

39 625 nm and 417 nm

40 37 cm, 94 cm

41 (*a*) 0.60 mrad (*b*) 6.0 mrad (*c*) 60 mrad

42   3.0 cm

43   (*a*) 1.53 km

44   9, 2*n* − 1

45   (*a*) 20.0 μm (*b*) 9

46   39

47   8

48   (*a*) 9 (*b*) 0.25

49 $\vec{E} = 3.6 A_0 \sin(\omega t - 0.98\,\text{rad})\boldsymbol{i}$

50 $\vec{E} = 6.1 A_0 \sin(\omega t + 0.43\,\text{rad})\boldsymbol{i}$

51 $I/I_0 = 0.0162$

52   (*b*) 3.33 mm

53   (*b*) 6.00 mm. The width for four sources is half the width for two sources.

54   (*a*) 242 mrad (*b*) $\theta_0 = 0$, $\theta_1 = \pm 80.1$ mrad, $\theta_2 = \pm 161$ mrad (*c*) 20.0 mrad
(*d*)

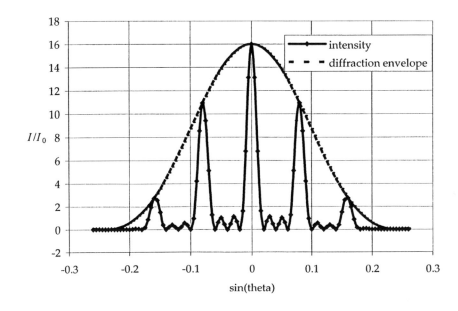

55

(a)

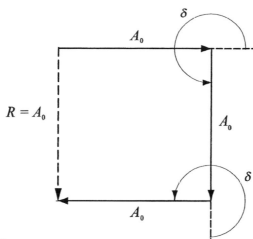

(b) 5.56 mW/m^2

56 At the three intensity minima $\phi = 2\pi$, 4π, and 6π, and at the three intensity maxima $\phi = 2.86\pi$, 4.92π, and 6.94π. At the intensity maxima $\phi \approx 3\pi$, 5π, and 7π.

57 (a) 8.54 mrad (b) 6.83 cm

58 8.54 cm

59 7.00 mm

60 (a) 49 m (b) Because L is inversely proportional to λ, The holes can be resolved better with violet light, which has a shorter wavelength. The critical angle for resolution is proportional to the wavelength. Thus, the shorter the wavelength, the farther away you can be and still resolve the two images.

61 5.00×10^9 m

62 9.9 mm

63 (a) 86.9 mrad, 82.1 mrad (b) 709 mrad, 662 mrad

64 485 nm, 658 nm

65 30.0°

66 (a) 0.02° (b) 1 mm

67 One can see the complete spectrum for only the first- and second- order spectra. That is, only for $m = 1$ and 2. Because 700 nm < 2 × 400 nm, there is no overlap of the second-order spectrum into the first-order spectrum; however, there is overlap of long wavelengths in the second-order spectrum with short wavelengths in the third-order spectrum.

68 13.0°

69 (*a*) 36.4 cm, 80.1 cm (*b*) 88.4 μm (*c*) 8000

70 3 cm

71 3.09×10^5, 5.14×10^4 cm^{-1}

73 (*a*) $\phi_{\mathrm{m}} = \frac{1}{2}\sin^{-1}\left(m\dfrac{\lambda}{d}\right)$ (*b*) 32.1°

75 3.5 μm

76 6.65°

77 3.6°, 2.5°

78 97 μm

79 (*a*) 15.1 cm (*b*) 3.33 m^{-1}

80 0.29°

81 0.13 mrad

82 115 nm

84 1.58

85 (*a*) 97.8 nm (*b*) No; because 180 nm is not in the visible portion of the spectrum. (*c*) 0.273

86 0.366 mm

87 12 m

88 (*a*) 1.000 292 (*b*) 1.000 291 56 ± 0.000 000 37